DATE DUE

MAI I 4 2014	
JUN 09 2014	

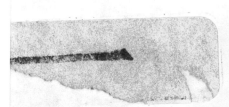

DEMCO, INC. 38-2931

Cell Ultrastructure

WILLIAM A. JENSEN

RODERIC B. PARK

University of California, Berkeley

Wadsworth Publishing Company, Inc., Belmont, California

Second printing: December 1967

L. C. Cat. Card No.: 67-21430

Printed in the United States of America

Preface

All organisms are composed of either single cells or aggregations of cells. These cells are the common denominator of biology and serve to unify the broad spectrum of life ranging from microorganisms to the complex higher plants and animals. Because cells are generally too small to be seen by the unaided human eye, we rely largely on microscopes for detailed information concerning cell structure. The results obtained with the light microscope during the past one hundred years provided a solid foundation on which ultrastructural studies with the electron microscope could be built. The purpose of this book is to summarize the advances in knowledge of cell structure that have taken place in the last ten years due to the use of electron microscopy.

In this book we offer a collection of electron microscope photographs of a wide range of cells and organisms. We have drawn examples from animals, plants, and bacteria, and have selected material prepared by a wide variety of techniques—sectioning, freeze-etching, shadowing, negative staining, and others.

In the selection of photographs, we have drawn on the work of many laboratories. Not all individual contributions can be covered, but we have tried to present micrographs by many of the outstanding electron microscopists of our time. We have also included numerous examples of our own work and that of our immediate colleagues.

This elementary introduction to the cell is intended to supplement the biology text used in beginning courses. We hope that it will bring to elementary biology courses the opportunity to appreciate cell structure in relation to form and function. The focal point of this book is the cell and its parts. The first chapter deals with general cell structure, and compares various types of cells. The next eleven chapters discuss the various cell parts and include a discussion of extracellular substances and viruses. The Appendix contains a description of the light and electron microscopes and the techniques of tissue preparation used with the electron microscope.

We have tried to extend the usefulness of the book by including two types of readings and references. First, general articles which are written on an introductory level and are easy to obtain. Second, more technical articles which are sources of additional information and references. In addition, the second group lists classic articles in which a new cell part was described or extensively studied for the first time.

We are extremely grateful to the many biologists who have so willingly provided us with the hard-won fruits of their labors with the electron microscope. A more cooperative group of individuals would be hard to imagine.

●

iii

Contents

Preface   iii

1   **The Cell**   1

2   **Membranes**   9

3   **Mitochondria**   13

4   **Chloroplasts**   16

5   **Lysosomes**   22

6   **Golgi Apparatus**   25

7   **Nucleus and Endoplasmic Reticulum**   30

8   **Ribosomes**   35

9   **Chromosomes and Cell Division**   38

10   **Microtubules and Flagella**   45

11   **Extracellular Structures**   48

12   **Viruses**   53

Appendix   56

1 The Cell

The cell, first seen and described by Robert Hooke in 1665, is the basic unit of the organization of all living organisms, whether they be minute plants, single celled animals, or huge organisms composed of millions of cells. Cells vary in many properties, such as size: some are small as microns, others large as meters. Some cells have an extremely simple internal organization, while others have an extremely intricate organization. Still, the remarkable similarities among cells have impressed biologists, for all cells share many properties and functions.

Every cell has a means of isolating its internal environment from the surrounding external environment. This isolating factor is accomplished by the *plasma membrane.* Plant cells and some animal cells have an additional coating, a rigid *cell wall,* which surrounds the exterior of the plasma membrane. The cell wall acts to protect and support the interior portions of the cells and impart strength to multicellular structures.

All cells have some means of releasing and transferring the energy necessary not only for growth, but also for maintaining their metabolic processes. All cells have a means of information retention and transfer which allows themselves and their progeny to be built in a meaningful and coherent fashion.

Two distinct types of cells make up living organisms. The first type, the *procaryotic cell,* utilizes the plasma membrane and the structures derived from it to perform a variety of functions without isolating these functions into individual units. The second type, the *eucaryotic cell,* utilizes a highly organized system of cell parts, which allows units of the cell to have distinct functions.

In procaryotic cells, such membrane localized functions as respiration and photosynthesis are continuous with or derived from the plasma membrane. These functions are not performed by separate cell units. The hereditary material, *desoxyribonucleic acid* (DNA), responsible for information storage and transfer, is also distributed through a large portion of the cell, the *nucleoplasm,* and is not separated from the remainder of the cell by a membrane system. This organization of the nucleoplasm is found in the bacteria and blue-green algae (Figs. 1–1 and 1–2). These cells are structurally relatively simple and the organisms that they constitute are simple in their overall morphology.

In the eucaryotic cell (Figs. 1–3, 1–4, 1–5), respiration and photosynthesis are packaged in discrete cell organelles. Organelles which perform photosynthesis are called *chloroplasts;* those which perform aerobic respiration are called *mitochondria.* Chloroplasts and mitochondria can be isolated from the cell, and their functions can then be studied. In a eucaryotic cell, the DNA—present in a highly organized form called the *chromosomes*—is contained in a membrane-bound structure called the *nucleus.* Within the nucleus is another body, the *nucleolus,* which is involved in information transfer functions.

Other functions of the cell, such as the excretion of cell wall material and other products, are associated with bodies called *dictyosomes.* The synthesis of proteins is associated with other cell parts—the *ribosomes* and the *endoplasmic reticulum* (ER). Still other structures are found in the cytoplasm of the eucaryotic cell. All organisms, except the bacteria and blue-green algae, are composed of eucaryotic cells—thus man, along with the giant redwood and the smallest protozoon, is an example of a eucaryotic organism (Figs. 1–3, 1–4, and 1–5).

The wide variety in form and function of the eucaryotic cell is illustrated in the following chapters. While the bulk of cells have but a single nucleus, there are many organisms in which many nuclei are present in a common cytoplasm. In addition, many cells develop highly specialized and limited functions. For example, the leaf cells of an oak tree contain chloroplasts and are involved in photosynthesis, while the root cells lack chloroplasts although other types of plastids are present. Similarly, in the human body, functional red blood cells lack a nucleus although they contain one in the early stages of their development.

As noted above, the various functions of the cell are compartmentalized in a variety of cell parts. Similarly, there is a division of labor between the cells within a multicellular organism. The cell is thus a highly efficient and adaptable unit for the maintenance and evolution of life. As such, it is worthy of attention in our attempt to understand organisms. ●

SUGGESTED READINGS

GENERAL

BOURNE, G. H. *Division of Labor in Cells.* New York: Academic Press, Inc., 1962. A short paperback containing recent data on the ultrastructure of cells.

BRACHET, J. "The Living Cell." *Scientific American,* September 1961. An excellent brief summary of our knowledge of the cell.

'ESPINASSE, MARGARET. *Robert Hooke.* Berkeley: University of California Press, 1962. A first-rate biography of a giant among early microscopists and the discoverer of the cell.

HUGHES, A. *A History of Cytology.* New York: Abelard-Schuman, Ltd., 1959. An excellent history of the early development of our knowledge of the cell.

JENSEN, W. A. *The Plant Cell.* Belmont, Calif.: Wadsworth Publishing Company, Inc., 1966. A short book on the structure and function of the plant cell.

KENNEDY, D. *The Living Cell.* San Francisco: W. H. Freeman & Company, 1965. A collection of articles from *Scientific American* on various aspects of the cell.

SWANSON, C. P. *The Cell.* Englewood Cliffs, N.J.: Prentice-Hall, Inc., 1964. A paperback on both plant and animal cells.

TECHNICAL

BRACHET, J., AND A. E. MIRSKY, EDS. *The Cell: Biochemistry, Physiology, Morphology.* New York: Academic Press, Inc., 1959–1964. Six volumes. A collection of articles summarizing our knowledge of the cell up to about 1960.

FAWCETT, D. W. *The Cell: Its Organelles and Inclusions. An Atlas of Fine Structure.* Philadelphia: W. B. Saunders Co., 1966. A collection of outstanding electron microscope photographs of mammalian cells.

FREY-WYSSLING, A., AND K. MÜHLETHALER. *Ultrastructural Plant Cytology.* New York: American Elsevier Publishing Co., 1965. A summary of the ultrastructure of the plant cell by one of the pioneers in the field.

PORTER, K. R., AND M. A. BONNEVILLE. *An Introduction to the Fine Structure of Cells and Tissues.* Philadelphia: Lea and Febiger, 1963. A collection of beautiful electron microscope photographs of mammalian cells. Professor Porter is an outstanding leader in the field.

RHODIN, J. A. G. *An Atlas of Ultrastructure.* Philadelphia: W. B. Saunders Co., 1963. A large collection of electron microscope pictures of mammalian tissues.

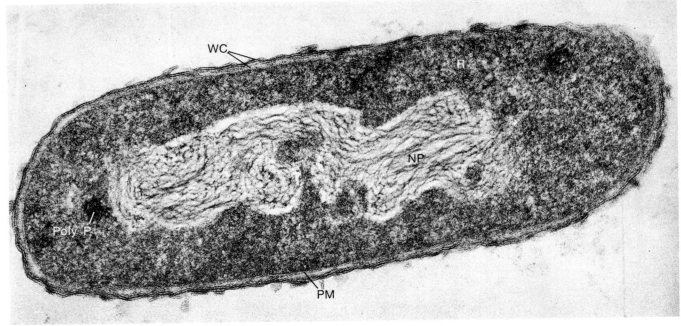

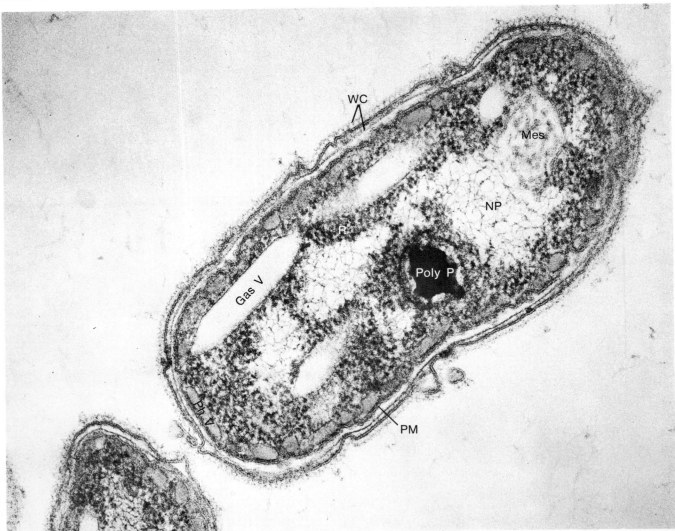

FIG. 1–1. The procaryotic cell, as illustrated by two bacterial cells. The upper cell is that of *Escherichia coli,* one of the world's most intensively studied organisms. The nucleoplasm (NP) occupies the center of the cell and contains the DNA. Numerous ribosomes (R) fill the rest of the cell. There are accumulations of polyphosphates (Poly P) present in the cell. The plasma membrane (PM) is poorly seen, but there is a distinct cell wall complex (WC). The lower cell is that of *Pelodictyon,* one of the most complex of bacteria. Besides the nucleoplasm (NP), ribosomes (R), plasma membrane (PM), polyphosphate (Poly P), and an elaborate cell wall complex (WC), there are gas vacuoles (Gas V), mesosomes (Mes), and, as this is a photosynthetic organism, photosynthetic vacuoles (PhV). The function of the mesosome is not known. Cells fixed in osmium and stained with lead. *Escherichia coli* ×28,000. *Pelodictyon* ×112,000. Photograph courtesy of Mrs. Cohen-Bazire, University of California, Berkeley.

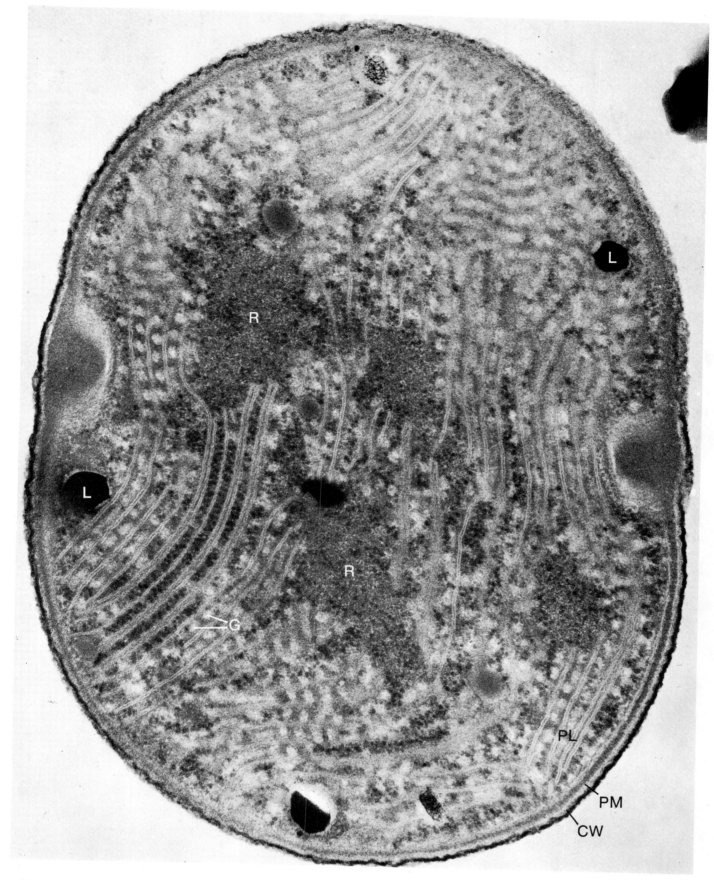

3

FIG. 1–2. Thin section of *Gleocapsa alpicola*, a unicellular blue-green alga. The cell was fixed in gluteraldehyde-osmium and post-stained with lead. The cell has extensive lamellar systems (the white lines) which contain the photosynthetic apparatus (PL). The dark, granular masses are ribosomes. The cell is surrounded by a relatively thin but obvious wall (CW) and a plasma membrane (PM). The small, white, round areas (G) are glycogen, a carbohydrate storage product, while the intense black areas are lipid or fat reserves (L). ×108,000. Photograph courtesy of Dr. Mary Allen, University of California, Berkeley.

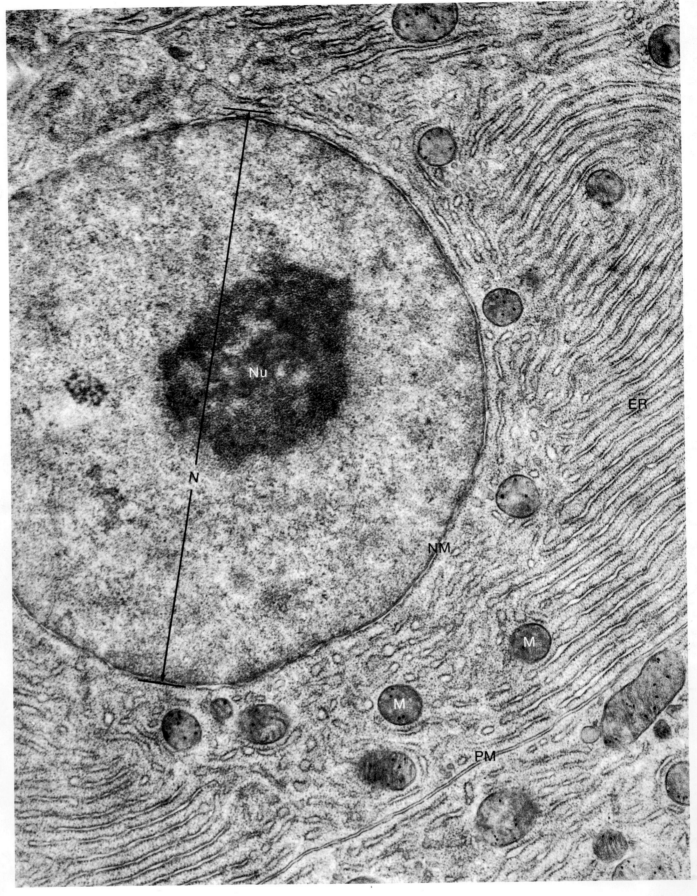

4

FIG. 1–3. A cell from the pancreas of the bat. The various functions of this cell are neatly compartmentalized relative to the condition found in the bacteria and blue-green algae. The nucleus (N), containing the chromosomes, DNA, and nucleolus (Nu), occupies a major portion of the cell and is limited by the nuclear membrane (NM). Long sheets of ER with ribosomes attached are present. Mitochondria (M), the site of oxidative metabolism, are evident. A portion of the plasma membrane (PM) delimiting the cell is visible. Osmium fixation. ×29,000. Photograph courtesy of Dr. Donald Fawcett, Harvard University School of Medicine. Dr. Fawcett is one of the foremost electron microscopists of animal tissue and he has greatly expanded our knowledge of the cell.

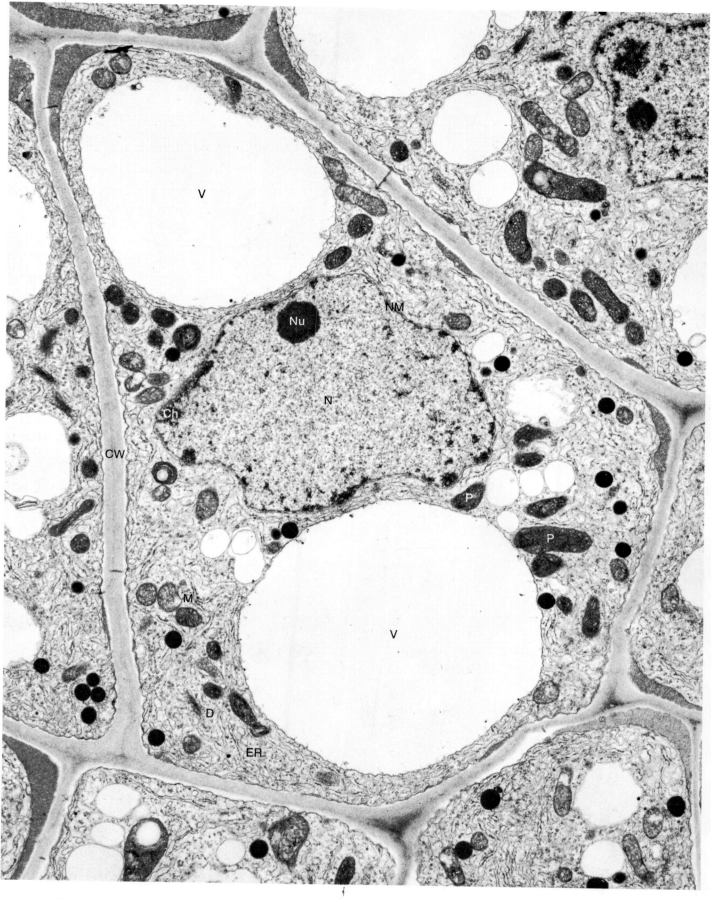

FIG. 1–4. The ultrastructure of the higher plant cell. This is a parenchyma cell from the developing fruit of cotton. The most distinguishing features are the large vacuoles (V) and the prominent cell wall (CW). In many plant cells, the vacuoles are even larger and the wall thicker. The nucleus (N) occupies the center of the cell and is delimited by the nuclear membrane (NM). A portion of a nucleolus (Nu) is visible, and chromatin (Ch) is seen adjacent to the nuclear membrane. The cytoplasm contains mitochondria (M), dictyosomes (D), and plastids (P). The plastids are not chloroplasts as this tissue is not green. There are considerable amounts of endoplasmic reticulum (ER) and ribosomes. The ribosomes are not seen clearly at this magnification. The composition and function of the round black bodies are unknown. The cell is surrounded by a plasma membrane. The cell was fixed in gluteraldehyde-osmium and stained with uranium and lead. ×12,800. Photograph courtesy of Mrs. Paula Stetler, University of California, Berkeley.

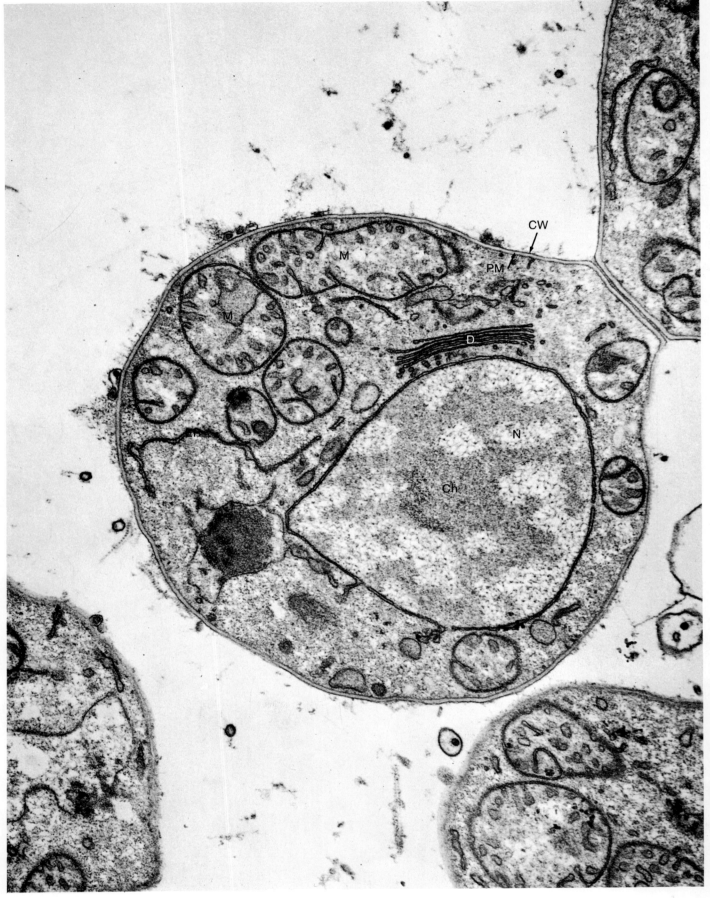

FIG. 1–5. Section through a uninucleate fungal cell of *Rhizidiomyces* sp. This is the stage of cell development immediately following the motile spore stage. The mitochondria (M) are particularly large and prominent. There is little ER and one conspicuous dictyosome (D). Chromatin (Ch) regions of the nucleus (N) are visible. The shape of the nucleus is related to a recently concluded motile stage. The plasma membrane (PM) and a thin cell wall (CW) surround the cell. The cell was fixed in KMnO₄. Ribosomes are not preserved by this method. ×48,000. Photograph courtesy of Dr. M. S. Fuller, Department of Botany, University of California, Berkeley.

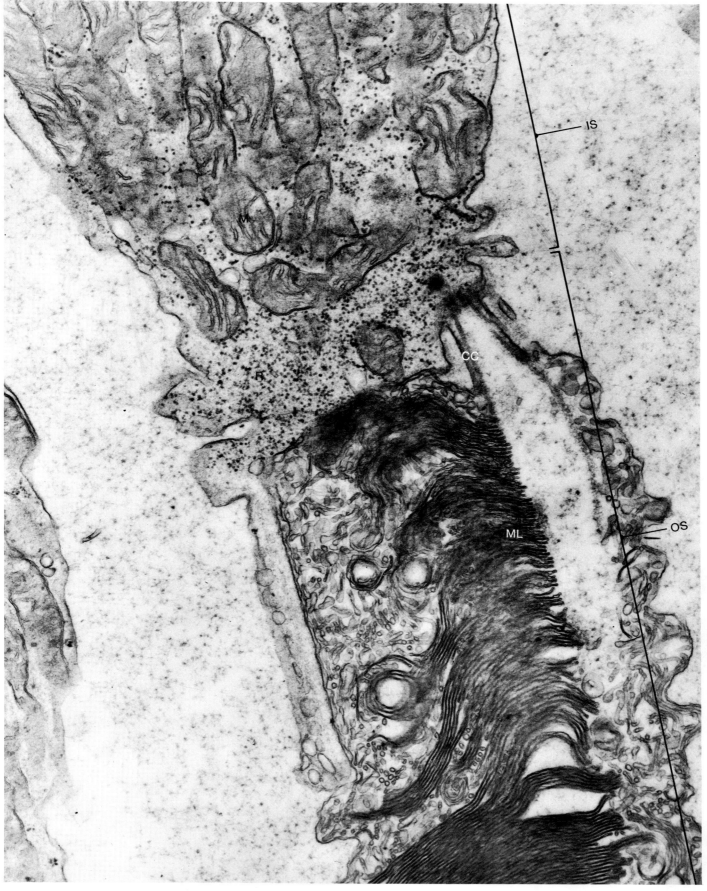

7

FIG. 1–6. Longitudinal section of a cone of the human retina, showing the outer segment (OS), connecting cilium (CC), and the inner segment (IS). The outer segment contains the membranous lamellae (ML), which are the site of photoreceptor pigments. The connecting cilium is a flagellar structure believed to be homologous with a flagellum and derived from flagellated cells in the embryo. The inner segment contains the nucleus, mitochondria (M), ribosomes (R), and other cell parts.

The retina of the vertebrate eye is an extraordinarily sensitive photoreceptor. As few as five quanta absorbed by the human retina are translated into a nerve impulse which is detected by the brain. The receptor system is built of rod and cone cells, each of which contains visual pigment which undergoes a photochemical change when light is absorbed. Pigment in the photoreceptors is located in the membrane systems in the outer segments of the cell. The mechanism by which the absorption of light in a few widely separated rods is detected and transmitted through the inner segment to the synapse is not known. Tissue fixed in osmium and stained with lead. ×38,000. Photograph courtesy of Dr. E. Yamada, Oak Ridge National Laboratory.

FIG. 1–7. Longitudinal section of a myofibril (Mf) of striated muscle of a rabbit. The main repeating unit is the sarcomere (Sar) which is 2.5 to 3 microns in length. The relatively dark areas comprise the A band, and the light areas bracketing the Z line make up the I band. The I band consists of thin filaments composed of actin while the thick filaments of the A band are myosin. Bridges connect the thin actin filaments to the thicker myosin filaments (arrows). The addition of ATP and magnesium to an isolated myofibril results in the movement of the Z lines closer to the A bands which do not shorten. Mitochondria (M) are located between the myofibrils. ×140,000. Photograph courtesy of Dr. H. E. Huxley, Cambridge University.

2   Membranes

In all cells the protoplasm is surrounded by a membrane. In both procaryotic and eucaryotic cells, plasma membranes, about 100 A* in thickness, serve to separate the contents of the cell from the external environment. In the eucaryotic cell, membranes also serve to compartmentalize the cytoplasm by delimiting various organelles. However, membranes do more than provide boundaries, for they are the site of many complex biochemical processes. These processes include active uptake of organic and inorganic substances, selection and exclusion of certain ions at the cell surface, oxidative and photosynthetic phosphorylation, quantum conversion in photosynthesis, and action potential propagation in nerves. Membrane processes have been difficult to study because these reactions occur within a highly structured and complex environment. The techniques used to elucidate mechanisms of solution reactions, which form the core of biochemical research, are often of little use in solving problems involving membranes. However, recent advances in the study of membrane morphology are providing new insights into possible explanations of these elusive phenomena.

The highly magnified region of the *Chlorella* cell, shown in Fig. 2–1, demonstrates some typical features of eucaryotic membranes. The plasma membrane in this *Chlorella* cell is about 75 A in thickness. With permanganate staining, it usually appears to consist of two dark layers, each about 25 A in width, separated by a third layer of lightly stained space of 25 A. This membrane structure occurs in all living things and has been designated by Robertson as "the unit membrane." The general structure of the unit membrane was predicted thirty years ago by Danielli and Davson mainly to explain physiological properties of membranes. Robertson has refined this original model, as shown in Diagram 2–1. The unit membrane consists of a bimolecular lipid layer covered on each side with a layer of protein. The water soluble, or polar, ends of the lipid face outward and contact the surface protein films. This model is supported by many electron micrographs of membranes, such as the nerve myelin shown in Fig. 2–2.

Some morphological evidence obtained during the past five years indicates that the much quoted Danielli-Davson

*A = 1 angstrom or 10⁻⁸ cm.

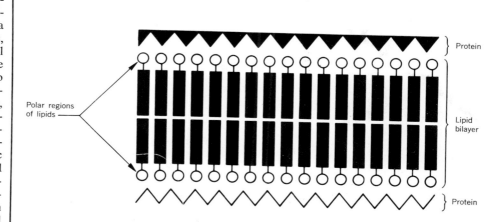

DIAGRAM 2–1. Cross section of the unit membrane. Total thickness 75–100 A.

9

model is not sufficient to explain the structure of all membranes. This new information comes primarily from techniques which give extended surface views of membranes, such as shadow casting, freeze-etching, and negative staining (see Appendix). Branton at the University of California has shown that in the freeze-etch technique membranes, when frozen, tend to split down the center.

Figure 2–3 is a comparison of the freeze-etch image of the internal membranes of a chloroplast and the myelin sheath of a frog sciatic nerve. The internal faces exposed by freeze-etching in these two membranes are totally different. Myelin presents a surface that could be predicted from the unit membrane model. Chloroplasts, on the other hand, are composed almost entirely of micellar regions which are distributed along the interior of the membrane. A model of the chloroplast membrane, then, is a series of micelles embedded in the membrane matrix. The membranes with the least complex functions, such as myelin, appear to be the least micellar in character, while those with the most complex functions, such as chloroplasts, present a more micellar appearance. Other biological membranes viewed in freeze-etching represent the intermediate stages between the two extremes represented by myelin and chloroplasts.

Understanding the chemical composition and function of these micelles may be an important key to understanding the mechanism of many membrane functions. ●

SUGGESTED READINGS

GENERAL

BRANTON, D., AND R. B. PARK. *Collected Papers on Membranes.* Boston: Little, Brown and Company (in preparation).

KORN, E. D. "Structure of Biological Membranes." *Science,* Vol. 153 (1966), pp. 1491–1498. A criticism of Robertson's unit membrane theory.

ROBERTSON, J. D. "The Membrane of the Living Cell." *Scientific American,* April 1962. A short summary of the unit membrane concept of the cell.

TECHNICAL

DANIELLI, J. F., AND H. DAVSON. "A Contribution to the Theory of Permeability of Thin Films." *J. Cell. and Comp. Physiol.,* Vol. 5 (1935), pp. 495–508. A classic paper on membrane structure which remains a major influence in membrane research today.

ROBERTSON, J. D. "The Molecular Structure and Contact Relationships of Cell Membranes." *Progress in Biophysics and Biophysical Chemistry,* Vol. 10 (1960), pp. 344–418. A review of the evidence for the unit membrane.

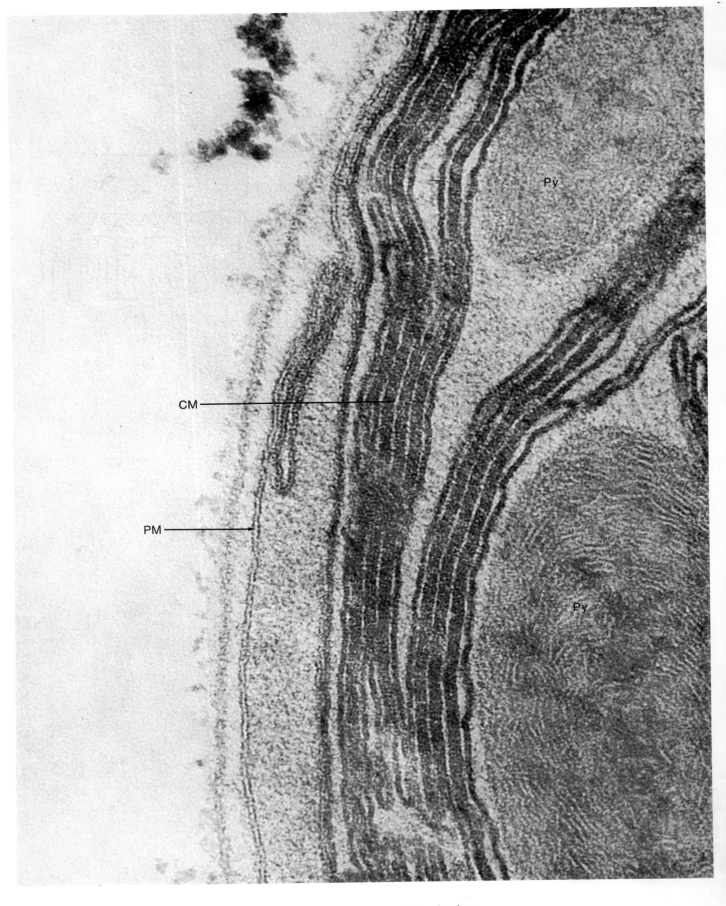

FIG. 2–1. A thin section of the unicellular green algae *Chlorella pyrenoidosa* fixed and stained with KMnO₄. An arrow (PM) points to the plasma membrane which demonstrates "unit membrane" structure. A second arrow (CM) points to chloroplast internal membranes which appear more micellar in character. The large layered structures (Py) are fatty pyrenoids which resemble myelin structures. ×240,000. Photograph, Dr. R. B. Park.

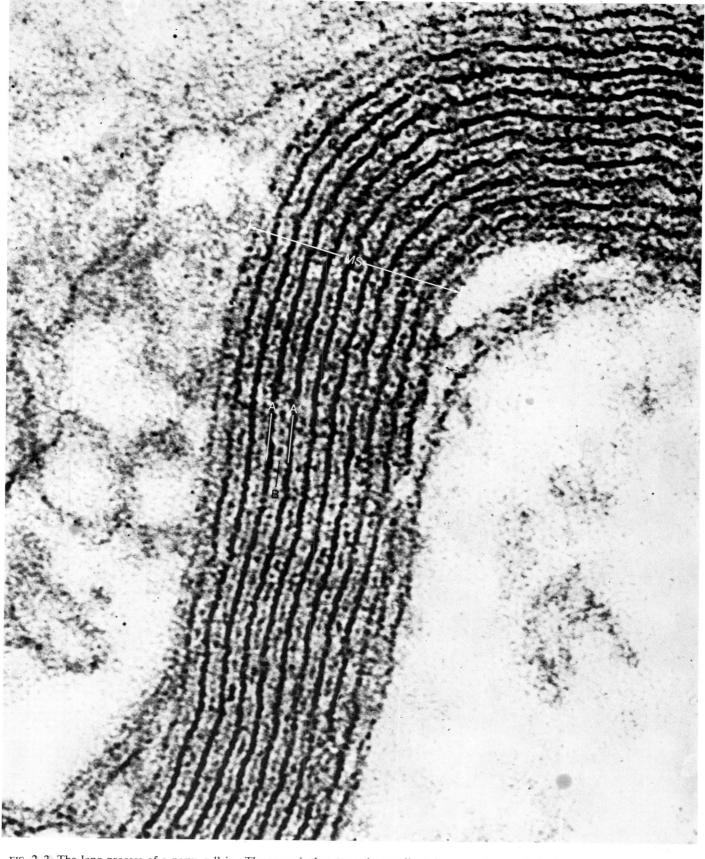

11

FIG. 2–2. The long process of a nerve cell is called the axon. The nerve impulse passes along the membrane surrounding the axon. The axon is surrounded by a second cell called the Schwann cell. In the membranes with high impulse transmission rates, the Schwann cells engulf the axon with their plasma membranes in a circular fashion yielding a coating many membranes thick. The nerve is then termed a myelinated nerve fiber. This myelin sheath (MS) may obtain great thickness, as shown in Fig. 2–3. The alternating thick and thin lines represent the boundary between two membrane surfaces and are alternately the two inside and two outside boundaries. The difference in staining is one indication that the outside and inside surfaces of the Schwann cell membrane differ in chemical character. The distance AA is 178 A and the distance AB or A′B is 89 A, the thickness of one membrane. Myelin is probably one of the simplest membranes which function primarily as insulators. Photograph courtesy of Dr. H. Fernandez-Moran, University of Chicago.

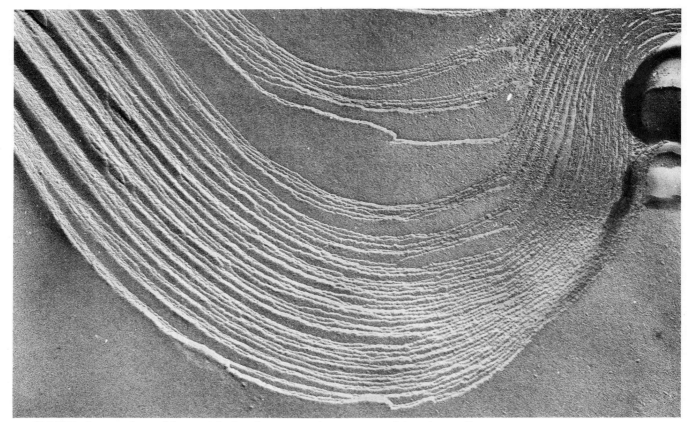

FIG. 2–3a. The fracture faces of freeze-etched myelin. These faces are interior views of the membrane, since in freeze-etching the frozen membrane splits down the center. The myelin membrane is largely non-micellar in character and presents an internal smooth face which would be predicted by the unit membrane model. ×80,000. Photograph courtesy of Dr. D. Branton, University of California, Berkeley.

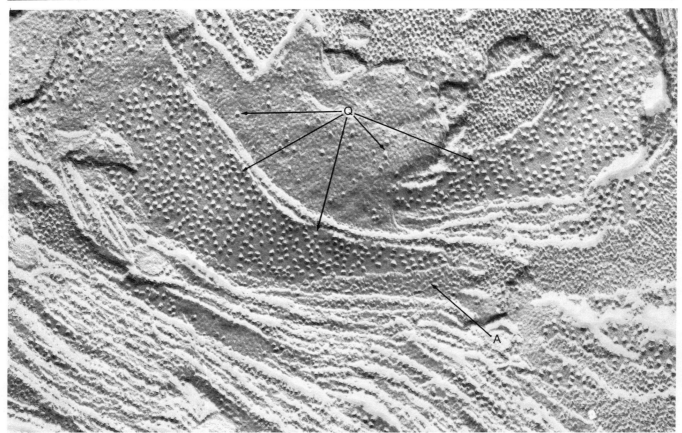

FIG. 2–3b. The fracture faces of freeze-etched chloroplast internal membranes. These faces are largely interior views of membranes. This membrane is extremely micellar in character. The large particles (170 A × 90 A) (Q) are buried within the intact membrane and are exposed by the fracture process. The face designated A in the membrane is actually the exterior of the membrane. It is seen here because it is tightly appressed to another internal membrane, the only condition under which fractures occur along a membrane surface. These micellar membrane faces were not predicted by the unit membrane model. ×90,000. Photograph courtesy of Drs. D. Branton and R. B. Park, University of California, Berkeley.

12

3   Mitochondria

In eucaryotic cells the mitochondrion is the site of respiration and fatty acid metabolism. When mitochondria were first reported by light microscopy, over eighty years ago, their function was unknown. In 1890, Altmann referred to them as bioblasts (life germs), implying that they might be the ultimate living things. This idea was strongly criticized; however, recent investigations indicate that Altmann may have been partially correct. The name, mitochondrion, derived from the Greek words for thread and grain, was given to these structures by Benda in 1897. In 1934, at the Rockefeller Institute in New York, Claude isolated mitochondria from rat liver in salt medium. He called them large granules rather than mitochondria because they would not stain with Janus green B, a characteristic stain for *in vivo* mitochondria.

Meanwhile, biochemists found that the respiratory enzymes were not easily solubilized in cell homogenates. They appeared to be bound together in an organized structure which sedimented with Claude's large granule fraction. By 1948 it was apparent that the mitochondrion, the large granule fraction, and the respiratory system were in fact the same organelle. In addition, it was discovered that the large granules would stain with Janus green B if they were isolated in sugar rather than in salt medium. Subsequently, it was shown that the large granule fraction was indistinguishable from *in vivo* mitochondria when viewed in the electron microscope.

The ultrastructure of the mitochondrion in thin section is shown in Fig. 3–1. It consists of two membranes: an outer membrane and an inner membrane which invaginates into the interior of mitochondrion to form *cristae*. These invaginations may take either the form of sheets or of tubules (Fig. 3–2), and they are most abundant in mitochondria associated with tissue of high metabolic activity. Mitochondria from tissue with high metabolic activity also have the highest ratio of respiratory enzymes to mitochondrial substance.

Biochemical data show that the enzymes of the tricarboxylic acid cycle reside in the intercristal space of the mitochondrion, while the enzymes carrying electrons from pyridine nucleotide to oxygen with accompanying phosphorylation lie in the cristal membrane system itself. From the evidence provided by freeze-etch and negative staining, this membrane system appears to consist of sub-units about 100 A in diameter. In the micrograph of such a negative stained preparation, shown in Fig. 3–2 (insert), small lollipops are evident on the membrane surface. The ball on the end of the stick is approximately 100 A in diameter and, with its adhering stalk and membrane, was called an elementary particle by Fernandez-Moran and Green.

Recent evidence indicates that more than one elementary particle may be required to form the electron transport pathway leading from pyridine nucleotide to oxygen. Although these particles are evident in negative stained preparations, there is some doubt that they represent true *in vivo* structures, for these particles may be partially due to artifacts occurring during the specimen preparation. In any case, the uniform distribution of these particles on the surface indicates they are a reflection of some real repeating unit along the cristal membrane of the mitochondrion. This conclusion has been substantiated by observations made by the freeze-etching technique.

Most biologists now agree that mitochondria as well as chloroplasts, discussed in the next chapter, contain DNA which differs from the DNA in the nucleus of the eucaryotic cell (Fig. 4–2). Mitochondrial DNA is not organized into a nucleus but is present in an interior nuclear area as a circular strand. These facts, combined with our knowledge that mitochondria can increase in number by a fission process, suggest that mitochondria are closely related to procaryotic organisms. We might assume, therefore, that the outer membrane of the mitochondrion is in fact synthesized with genetic information from the nucleus of the eucaryotic host, while the inner membrane of the mitochondrion is synthesized with information from the mitochondrial DNA. Thus, the inner membrane of the mitochondrion might actually represent a derivative of the plasma membrane of a former procaryotic parent. The much derided "bioblast" of Altmann may be a more valid concept than has been generally believed.

In the following chapter you will see that the functions and origins of the mitochondrion, as well as the ultrastructure, are closely related to those of the chloroplast.

•

SUGGESTED READINGS

GENERAL

GREEN, D. E. "The Mitochondrion." *Scientific American,* January 1964. A controversial and stimulating view of the structure and function of the mitochondria.

LEHNINGER, A. L. *The Mitochondrion.* New York: W. A. Benjamin, Inc., 1964.

TECHNICAL

FFRNANDEZ-MORAN, H., ET AL. "A Macromolecular Repeating Unit of Mitochondrial Structure and Function." *J. Cell. Biol.,* Vol. 22 (1964), pp. 63–100. An attempt to associate mitochondrial function with morphological ultrastructure.

PALADE, G. E. "Electron Microscopic Study of Mitochondrial Structure." *J. Histo. and Cytochemistry,* Vol. 1 (1953), p. 188. This is one of the classical papers on the ultrastructure of the cell.

PARSONS, D. F. "Mitochondrial Structure: Two Types of Subunits on Negatively Stained Mitochondrial Membranes." *Science,* Vol. 140 (1963), pp. 985–987.

SMITH, DAVID. "The Organization of Flight Muscle in an Aphid *Megoura viciae* (Homoptera)." *J. Cell Biol.,* Vol. 27 (1965), p. 379.

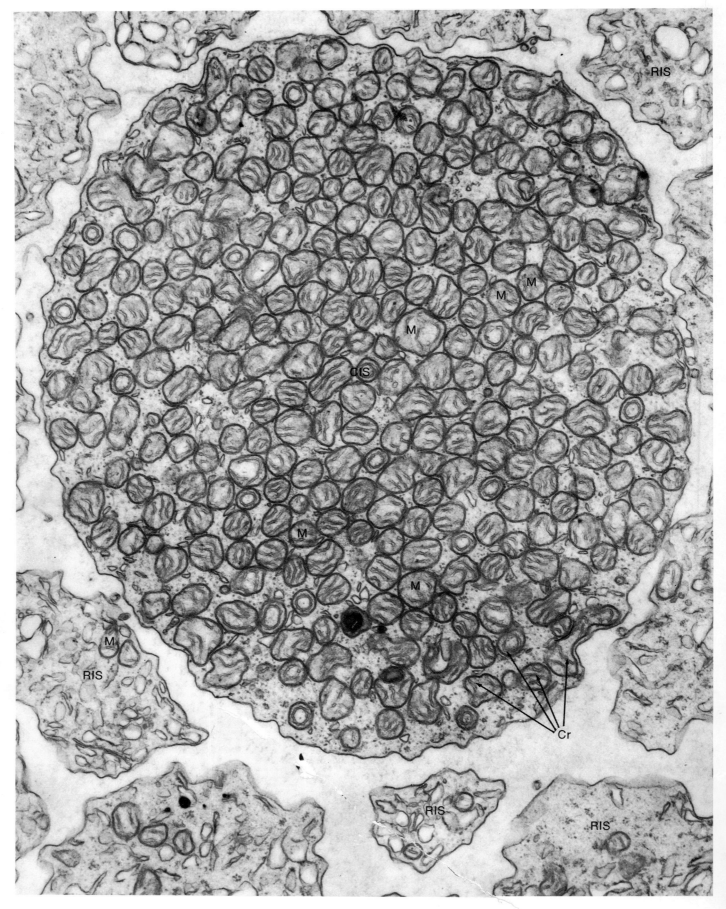

FIG. 3–1. Tangential section of human retina showing rod inner segments (RIS) and cone inner segments (CIS). Numerous mitochondria (M) are present in these regions of cone cells. The cristae (Cr) assume a number of forms ranging from tubular to branched. See Fig. 1–6 for a longitudinal view of the same mitochondria. ×26,000. Photograph courtesy of Dr. E. Yamada, Oakridge National Laboratory.

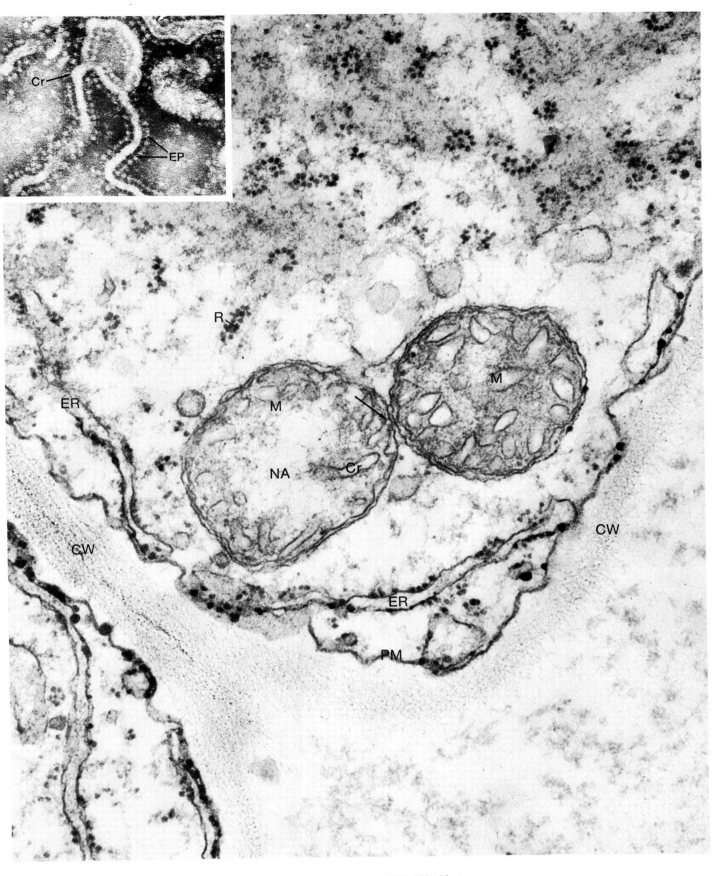

15

FIG. 3–2. Thin section of gluteraldehyde-osmium fixed cotton cell. Two mitochondria (M) are evident in the cell cytoplasm. The mitochondria contain numerous tubular cristae characteristic of plant material, some of which are continuous with the mitochondrial inner membrane (arrow). Strands of DNA are visible in the mitochondria (NA). Also evident in this micrograph are the cell wall (CW), ribosomes (R), and endoplasmic reticulum (ER). Many of the cristae appear as tubules, though some are continuous with the mito- chondrial inner membrane. X74,000. Photograph, Dr. W. A. Jensen.

INSERT: A negatively stained preparation of osmotically swollen mitochondria. When treated in this way the cristae (Cr) appear tubular and covered with 100 A diameter particles on 40 A stalks. These are called elementary particles (EP) and may be related to functional respiratory units in the cristae. ×92,000. Photograph courtesy of D. F. Parsons, University of Toronto.

4 Chloroplasts

The photosynthetic apparatus of eucaryotic cells is contained within an organelle called the chloroplast. The chloroplast is one of a family of plastids found in plant cells; other plastids are involved in the storage of reserve food stuffs (Fig. 4–2) or contain pigments of colored plant parts, as in flowers. As shown in Figs. 4–1 and 3–2, the chloroplast is surrounded by two membranes (sometimes called a double membrane). It often appears that the outer membrane is similar to the plasma membrane of the cell, whereas the inner membrane is similar to the internal membrane system of the chloroplast. One interpretation of this situation is that the outer membrane is derived from the parent cell as a means of isolating itself from the chloroplast. Thus, the inner membrane serves to contain the chloroplast material. As with mitochondria, chloroplasts have recently been found to contain DNA which differs from the nuclear DNA.

The internal portion of the chloroplast is divided into two main parts, the membrane system and its embedding matrix (Fig. 4–1). The membrane system is made up of closed flattened sacs called *thylakoids* (from the Greek meaning sac-like). The thylakoid membrane contains the chlorophyll and the quantum conversion apparatus of eucaryotic cells. The thylakoid is also the site of oxygen evolution and photosynthetic phosphorylation. This membrane is composed of micellar subunits (*quantasomes,* Fig. 4–4) and participates in electron transport from water to pyridine nucleotide cofactors. The membrane embedding matrix or stroma material of the chloroplasts contains the enzymes responsible for fixation of carbon dioxide into sugar and the ribosomes involved in chloroplast protein synthesis.

The thylakoids may assume many configurations ranging from those in which the thylakoids are widely separated, as in red algae (Fig. 4–3), to the highly complex situation shown in Fig. 4–1. The structure produced when several *small thylakoids* or *grana lamellae* are stacked one on top of the other is called a *granum.* The membrane structures extending between the grana stacks are called *large thylakoids* or *stroma lamellae.* Certain grasses have some chloroplasts which contain grana stacks similar to the chloroplast shown in Fig. 4–1 and other chloroplasts which contain only the large thylakoids. However, all these chloroplasts are capable of quantum conversion and photosynthesis, and the significance of the various thylakoid configurations is presently unknown.

Chloroplasts in lower plants are formed by the division of the mature chloroplast. In higher plants, on the other hand, chloroplasts appear to arise from a much smaller body which reproduces by division. This smaller body is called a *proplastid* and contains *protochlorophyll.* If a higher plant grows in the dark, the proplastids do not fully develop. They are arrested at the stage of development shown in Fig. 4–5. The paracrystalline structures shown within these cells are called *prolamellar bodies.* When the plant is placed in light, these bodies break down and give rise to the lamellar system of the chloroplast. If a higher plant is left in continuous light, the thylakoids appear to arise by invagination of the inner chloroplast membrane.

Chloroplasts as well as mitochondria are involved in electron transport, perform phosphorylations, contain DNA, reproduce by division, and, in many ways, resemble a procaryotic-like organism which has invaded the eucaryotic cell. ●

SUGGESTED READINGS

GENERAL

BASSHAM, J. A. "The Path of Carbon in Photosynthesis." *Scientific American,* June 1962, pp. 88–100. The emphasis in this brief paper is on the carbon fixation reactions in photosynthesis.

BOGORAD, L. "Photosynthesis." In W. A. Jensen and L. G. Kavaljian, eds., *Plant Biology Today,* 2nd edition (Belmont, Calif.: Wadsworth Publishing Company, Inc., 1966). An excellent, readable summary of our knowledge of photosynthesis related to chloroplast structure.

PARK, R. B. "The Chloroplast." In J. Bonner and J. Varner, eds., *Plant Biochemistry* (New York: Academic Press, Inc., 1965), Chapter 9.

TECHNICAL

GANTT, E., AND S. F. CONTI. "The Ultrastructure of Porphyridium and Cruentum." *J. Cell Biol.,* Vol. 26 (1965), pp. 365–375.

GUNNING, B. E. S. "The Greening Process in Plastids." *Protoplasma,* Vol. 60 (1965), pp. 111–130.

PARK, R. B., AND N. G. PON. "Correlation of Structure with Function in *Spinacia oleracea* Chloroplasts." *J. Mol. Biol.,* Vol. 3 (1961), pp. 1–10.

SWIFT, H. "Nucleic Acids of Mitochondria and Chloroplasts." *Am. Naturalist,* Vol. 99 (1965), p. 201.

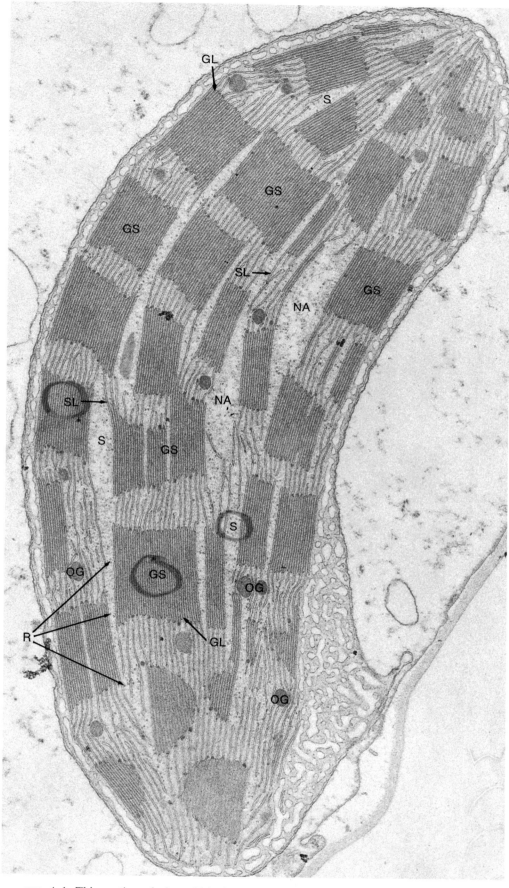

FIG. 4–1. Thin section of gluteraldehyde-osmium fixed corn leaf tissue showing a chloroplast in cross section. The internal membrane system contains chlorophyll and is the site of the light reactions and associated electron transport reactions of photosynthesis. This continuous membrane system can be divided into two morphological groupings: those membranes occurring only in grana stacks (GS) are called grana lamellae (GL) or small thylakoids, while those membranes connecting and traversing various grana stacks are called stroma lamellae (SL) or large thylakoids. The embedding matrix is called stroma (S) and contains the photosynthetic carbon cycle enzymes, ribosomes, and DNA of the chloroplast. Ribosomes (R), osmiophilic granules (OG), and DNA containing areas (NA) may also be seen in this micrograph. ×80,000. Photograph courtesy of Dr. L. K. Shumway, Washington State University.

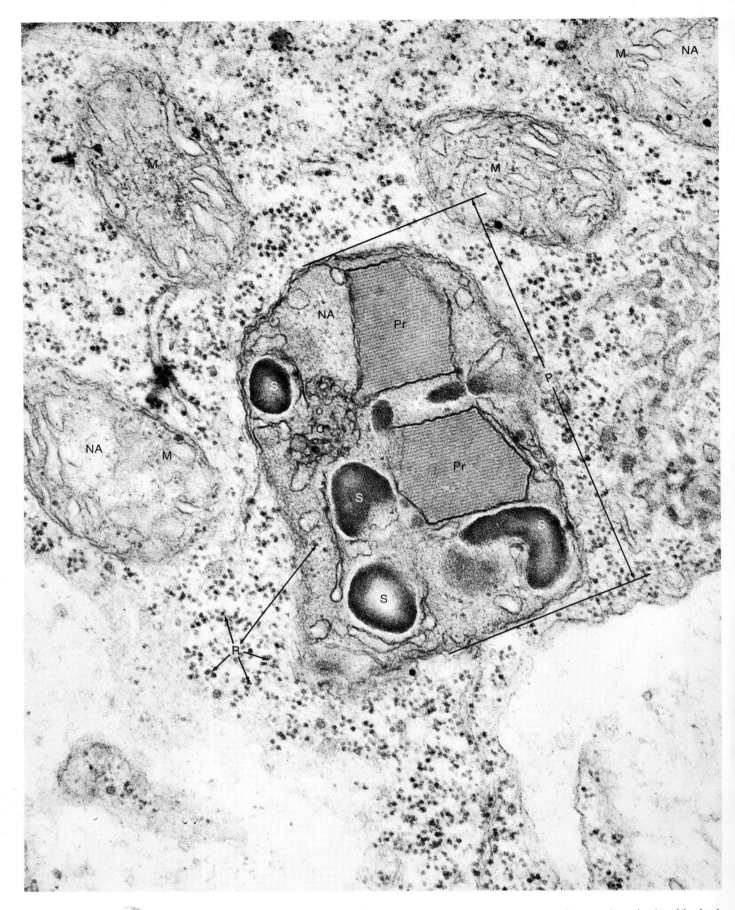

FIG. 4–2. A storage plastid (P) from bean root tip containing starch grains (S), crystalline proteins (Pr), and a tubular complex (TC) which is probably related to the prolamellar body shown in Fig. 4–5. There are ribosomes (R) evident in both the storage plastid and the surrounding cytoplasm. Presumed DNA containing areas (NA) are present both in the mitochondria (M) and in the storage plastid. Tissue fixed in gluteraldehyde-osmium and stained with lead. ×77,000. Photograph courtesy of Dr. E. Newcomb, University of Wisconsin.

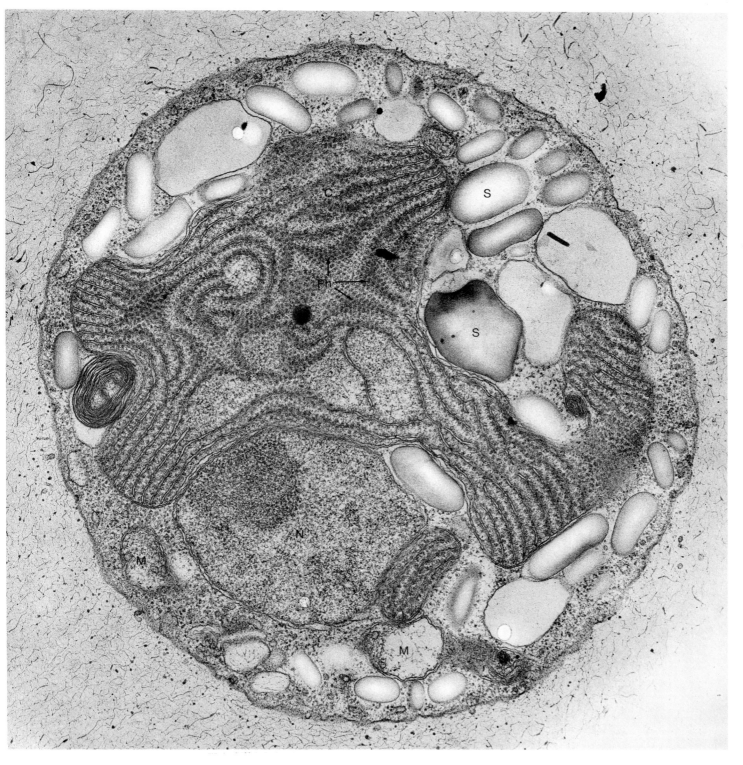

FIG. 4–3. A thin section of the red alga *Porphyridium cruentum* fixed and stained with gluteraldehyde and OsO$_4$. This cell contains many grains of storage polysaccharide (S), a chloroplast (C), mitochondria (M), and nucleus (N). The chloroplast contains phycoerythrin photosynthetic accessory pigments which account for the red color of the organism and appear to be located in the particles (Ph) on the surface of the thylakoids. The chlorophyll is contained within the thylakoid membrane. ×35,000. Photograph supplied by E. Gantt and S. F. Conti, Dartmouth Medical School.

20

FIG. 4–4. A heavy metal shadowed preparation of isolated spinach thylakoids. The 185 ×155 ×90 A micellar units embedded in these membranes are evident in this micrograph. Highly ordered arrays are the exception rather than the rule, the quantasomes generally occurring randomly in the membrane matrix. The random array is apparent in Fig. 2–3b. These particles are probably related to quantum conversion units within the membrane. Photograph, Dr. R. B. Park.

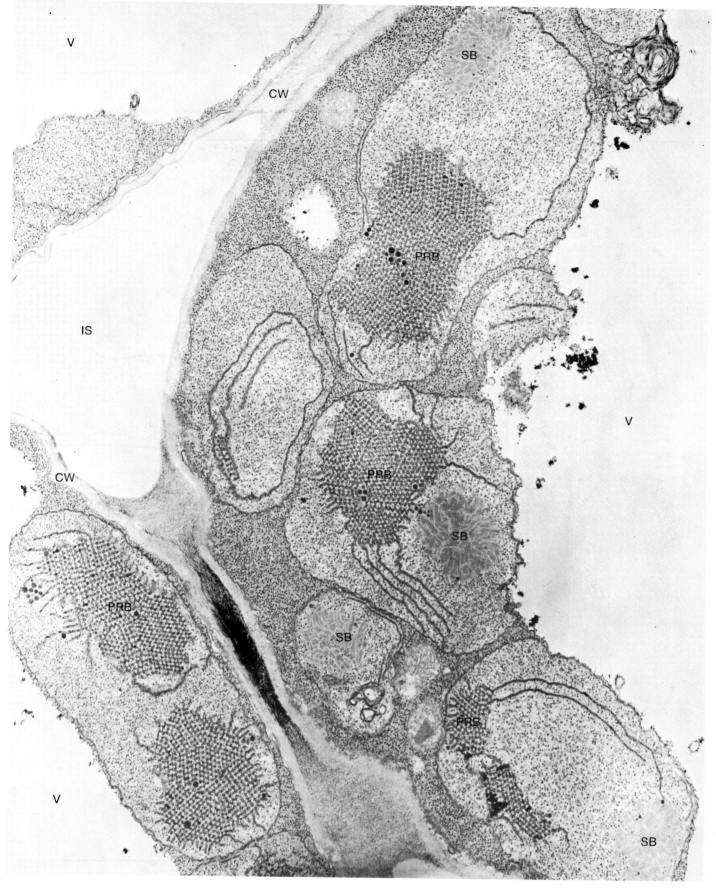

FIG. 4–5. Thin section of etiolated bean leaf fixed and stained with gluteraldehyde and osmium. The proplastids evident in this micrograph contain paracrystalline prolamellar bodies (PRB) which reform in the light when chlorophyll is produced into thylakoids. The proplastids also contain stroma bodies (SB) whose origin and function is not understood. Many ribosomes are evident both in the cytoplasm and in the proplastids. Other structures evident in this micrograph are the primary cell wall (CW), vacuoles (V), and intercellular space (IS). ×26,000. Photograph courtesy of Dr. B. E. S. Gunning, University of Belfast.

5 Lysosomes

The lysosomes were discovered in 1952. Thus far, they have been conclusively demonstrated only in animal cells and were described biochemically before they were described morphologically. Christian de Duve noted that in time mitochondrial preparations become increasingly rich in certain hydrolytic enzymes. These hydrolytic enzymes were being released by the breakdown of a contaminating vesicle in the mitochondrial preparation. This vesicle with its content of highly disruptive enzymes was the lysosome.

When viewed under the electron microscope a lysosome is a deceptively simple structure (Figs. 5–1 and 5–2). It is surrounded by a single membrane and may appear homogenous or slightly mottled inside. It contains a large number of hydrolytic enzymes, such as ribonuclease which breaks down ribonucleic acid, cathepsins which destroy proteins, phosphatases which break down phosphate compounds (Fig. 5–3), and many other enzymes of a similar nature.

Under normal conditions, the enzymes within the lysosome remain inactive and are not in contact with the substrates. However, if the membrane is damaged, the released enzymes will attack those parts of the cell which are composed of the enzymes' respective substrates. A change in the exterior or interior environment of the cell which causes the lysosome membrane to break and thus release enzymes is believed to be responsible for the death of certain cells.

In some cases this disintegration of the cell is correlated with morphogenic development. For instance, lysosomes play an important part in the regression of the tail portion of tadpoles as they develop into frogs. Lysosomes are also involved in *Amoeba,* for example, with the breakdown of ingested food particles.

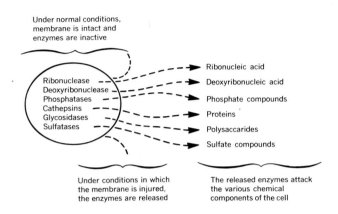

DIAGRAM 5–1. The lysosome concept.

The food enters the cell in the form of a vacuole composed of an invagination of the plasma membrane. The lysosome migrates to the edge of the food vacuole, and the membranes fuse so that the contents of the lysosome mix with those of the food vacuole. The enzymes then break down the ingested food into smaller units which enter the cell and which are utilized metabolically. In some cases, cell parts are digested within the cell by a similar means: a membrane originating from the endoplasmic reticulum usually forms around the cell part and the lysosome then empties into the particle.

Certain chemical substances, such as chloroquine (an anti-malaria drug) and cortisone, have been found to stabilize lysosomes, whereas vitamin A acts to destroy lysosomal membranes. The way in which these chemical substances interact with lysosomes explains some of their pharmaceutical activity. ●

SUGGESTED READINGS

GENERAL

DE DUVE, C. "The Lysosome." *Scientific American,* May 1963. An excellent summary of the available data on the form and function of the lysosomes, by the man who discovered them.

TECHNICAL

DE DUVE, C. "Lysosomes: A New Group of Cytoplasmic Particles." In T. Hayashi, ed., *Subcellular Particles* (New York: The Ronald Press Company, 1959). A classic paper summarizing the evidence for a new cell part.

NOVIKOFF, A. B., E. ESSNER, AND N. QUINTANA. "Golgi Apparatus and Lysosomes." *Federation Proceedings,* Vol. 23 (1964), pp. 1010–1022. A recent summary of current concepts on the function and origin of lysosomes in tissue. This is one of a series of papers from a symposium on lysosomes published in an issue of *Federation Proceedings.*

22

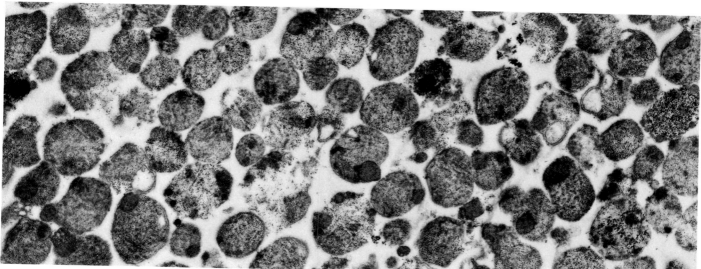

FIG. 5–1. Purified rat liver lysosomes. Pieces of rat liver had been carefully homogenized so that the cells were broken open but the cell parts preserved. Then, by centrifuging the suspension of cell parts at increasingly higher speeds, the cell parts can be separated. Special techniques and skill are needed to obtain lysosomes of the high purity shown in this picture. This photograph is of a pellet of isolated lysosomes formed in the bottom of a centrifuge tube. The pellet was fixed in osmium, embedded in methacrylate, sectioned, and stained with lead. Note the similarity of the isolated lysosomes to the one seen in a tissue section in Fig. 6–2. ×24,000. Photograph courtesy of Professor Christian de Duve, Rockefeller Institute, New York, and the University of Louvain, Belgium.

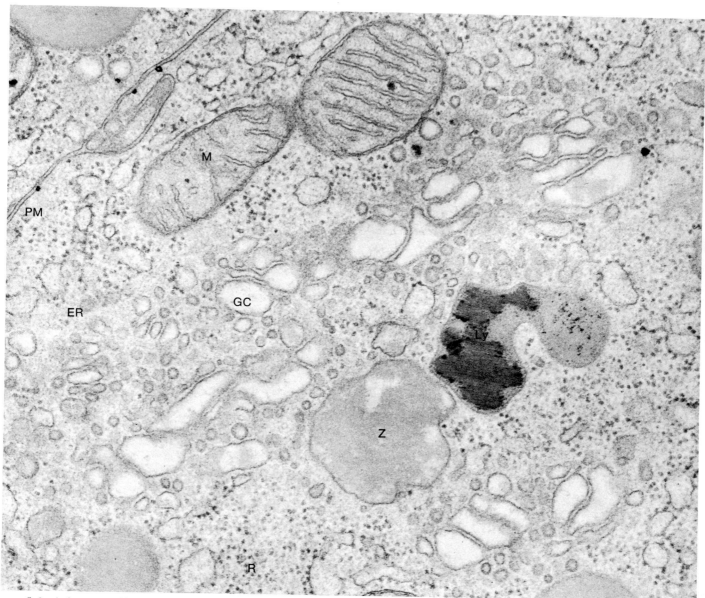

FIG. 5–2. A lysosome (Ly) in a section of guinea pig pancreas exocrine cell. The lysosome is seen close to the Golgi complex (GC) and a forming zymogen granule (Z). Mature zymogen granules are also present in the section. Zymogen granules contain inactive enzymes which are secreted from the cell. The enzymes then become active and are involved in digestion. The cell is rich in ribosomes (R) but relatively poor in endoplasmic reticulum (ER). Mitochondria (M) are present and a portion of the plasma membrane can be seen (PM). Osmium fixation, lead staining. ×57,000. Photograph supplied by Dr. George Palade, Rockefeller Institute, New York.

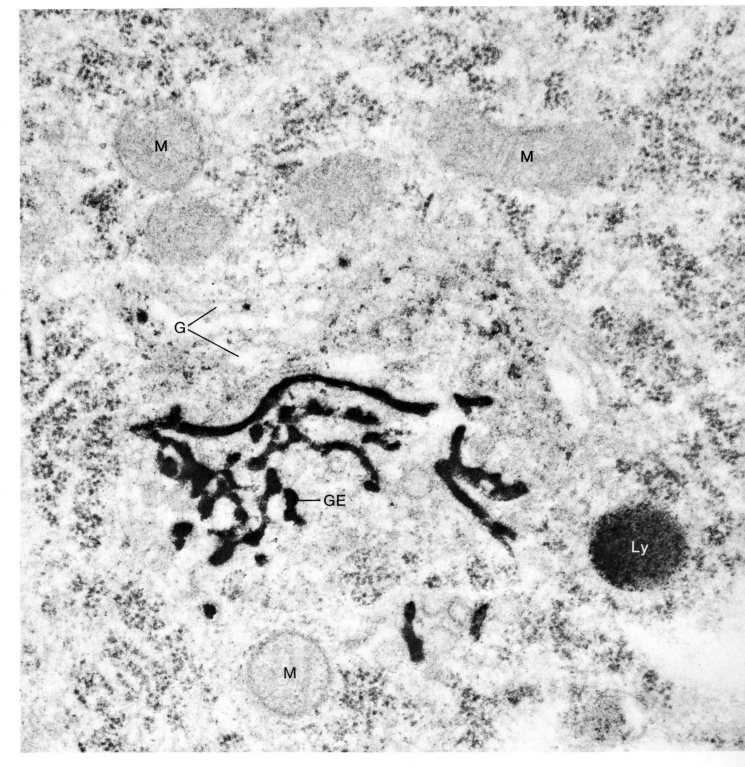

24

FIG. 5–3. A section of the dorsal root ganglion of a rat. This preparation shows the localization of the enzyme acid phosphatase, which is one of the characteristic enzymes found in lysosomes. Relatively thick sections of frozen tissue are cut and these are incubated at 37°C in thymidylic acid at pH 5.0 in the presence of lead. The enzyme splits the phosphate from the substrate, and the lead combines with liberated phosphate to form insoluble lead phosphate. This compound precipitates at or very near the site of the enzyme and, as the lead appears dark in electron microscope preparations, visualizes the site of the enzyme. Thus, in this photograph the very black areas represent sites that are rich in acid phosphatase activity. These are a lysosome (Ly) and a Golgi-associated region of the endoplasmic reticulum (GE). The mitochondria (M) and the Golgi vesicles (G) are free of reaction product. ×36,000. Photograph courtesy of Dr. Alex Novikoff, Albert Einstein College of Medicine. Professor Novikoff has pioneered the use of enzyme localization procedures on the ultrastructural level and has worked extensively on the formation of lysosomes and their role in cell function.

6   Golgi Apparatus

For years one of the most controversial cell parts was a complex of vesicles first observed by Golgi in 1903 while studying the nerve cells of the barn owl. These structures, called the Golgi apparatus, stained intensely with certain silver stains and were subsequently found in nerve and secretory tissue in many animals. Whether or not the Golgi apparatus existed in plant cells was long and hotly debated, as was its function and morphology in animal cells.

The electron microscope has shown the Golgi apparatus to be a complex structure in animals and has confirmed the existence of at least one type of Golgi apparatus in plants. In animals the form of the Golgi apparatus is highly variable but consists of smooth membranes, large vesicles, and small vesicles (Fig. 6–2). It also contains a type of organization so uniform that it has been given a special name—the *dictyosomes*. The dictyosomes consist of stacks of net-like tubules or vesicles surrounded by a halo of small spherical vesicles. Dictyosomes are found in all plant cells and are also found in many animal cells.

Secretion is one of the roles of the Golgi apparatus, particularly of the dictyosomes, in both plant and animal cells. An example of this is the secretion of wall materials in plant cells, as in the root cap cells (Fig. 6–1). It can be shown that the vesicles at the edge of the dictyosomes enlarge and move to the plasma membrane. Here the membrane of the vesicle first fuses with the plasma membrane and then the contents extrude from the cell and fuse with the cell wall. Autoradiographic experiments on the electron microscope level have conclusively shown that material is accumulated in the Golgi vesicles, that these vesicles do, in fact, move to the cell membrane, and that, subsequently, the same material is found in the cell wall. In animal cells which excrete material to the external environment these vesicles seem to be associated with the secretion of enzymes or other materials. In both plants and animals the Golgi apparatus, particularly the dictyosomes, seem to be a staging area for excretion of compounds from the cell rather than the site of synthesis of these materials. Much remains to be known about the structure and function of this interesting and elusive cell part. ●

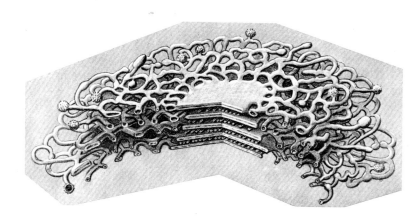

DIAGRAM 6–1. Interpretation of a portion of plant dictyosome composed of five cisternae. Cisternal maturation is depicted from top to bottom.

25

SUGGESTED READINGS

TECHNICAL

DALTON, A. J. "Golgi Apparatus and Secretion Granules." In J. Brachet and A. E. Mirsky, eds., *The Cell* (New York: Academic Press, Inc., 1959–1964), Vol. 2, p. 203. A summary of the role of the Golgi apparatus in animal cells.

MOLLENHAUER, H. H. "An Intercisternal Structure in the Golgi Apparatus." *J. Cell Biol.,* Vol. 24 (1965), p. 504. An excellent study of the fine structure of the Golgi apparatus.

———, AND D. J. MORRE. "Golgi Apparatus and Plant Secretory Processes." *Annual Review of Plant Physiology,* Vol. 17 (1966), pp. 27–46. A recent survey of the role of the Golgi apparatus in plant cells.

MORRE, D. J., AND H. H. MOLLENHAUER. "Isolation of the Golgi Apparatus from Plant Cells." *J. Cell Biol.,* Vol. 23 (1964), pp. 295–305.

WHALEY, W. G., J. E. KEPHART, AND H. H. MOLLENHAUER. "Developmental Changes in the Golgi Apparatus of Maize Root Cells." *Amer. J. Bot.,* Vol. 46 (1959), pp. 743–751. A classic paper on the role of the Golgi apparatus in plants.

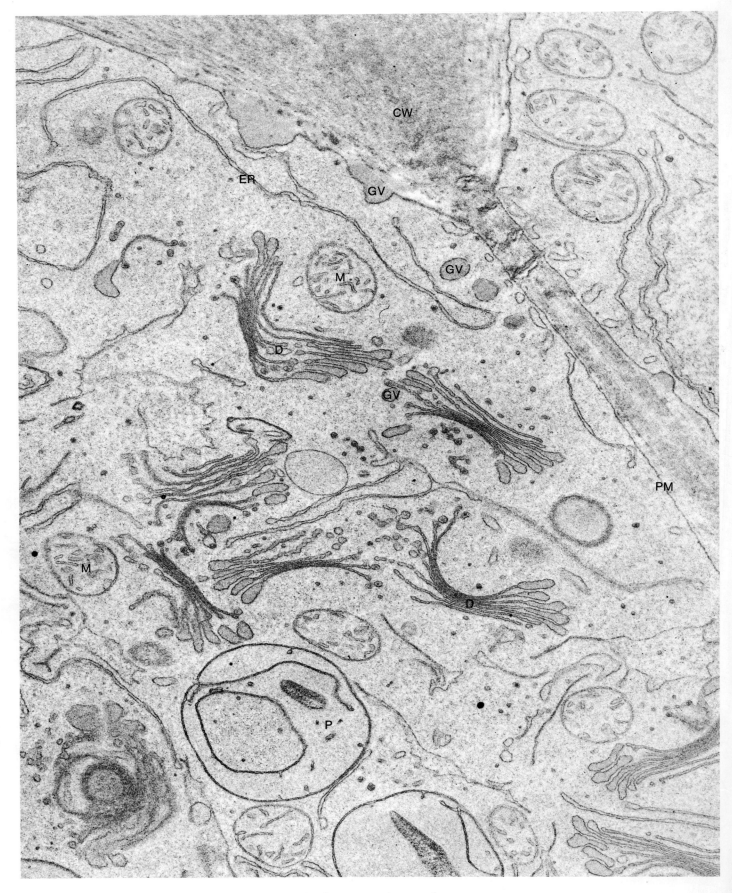

26

FIG. 6–1. Golgi apparatus (dictyosomes, D) in the root cap cells of corn. The vesicles (GV) are being produced at the end of the cisternae and are migrating to the edge of the cell, where they are fusing (arrow) with the existing wall (CW). Plastids (P), mitochondria (M), endoplasmic reticulum (ER), and the plasma membrane (PM) are visible in the photograph. Tissue fixed in KMnO₄, which removes the ribosomes and some other structures from the cells.

This photograph was obtained from the laboratory of Dr. W. Gordon Whaley through Dr. Hilton Mollenhauer. Professor Whaley's group at the University of Texas has pioneered in research relating the activity of the Golgi apparatus to the formation of walls in plant cells.

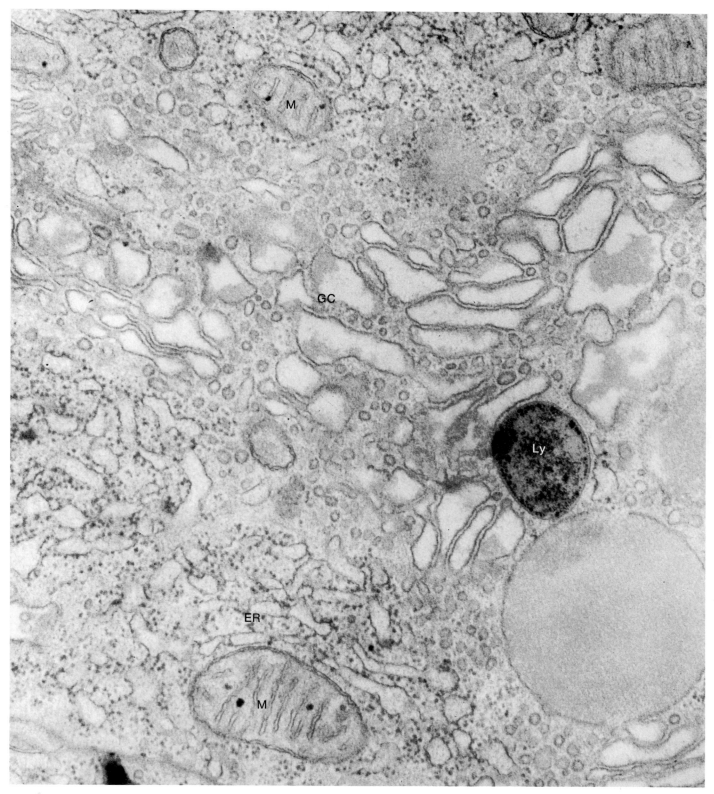

FIG. 6–2. The Golgi complex (GC) present in many animal cells is represented by this section of a cell from a guinea pig pancreas. The complex fills the entire center of the illustration and is seen associated with a lysosome (Ly). The Golgi complex shown appears much less tightly organized than those present in plant cells. Mitochondria (M) and endoplasmic reticulum (ER) with attached ribosomes are present in the cell. See also Fig. 5–2. Tissue fixed in osmium and stained with lead. ×60,000. Photograph courtesy of Dr. George Palade, Rockefeller Institute, New York.

28

FIG. 6–3. Freeze-etch view of two dictyosomes (D) in an onion root tip cell. The lower one (A) is seen in cross section while the upper one (B) is seen in face view. Note the open appearance of the cisternae (GC) of the dictyosomes and the numerous vesicles (GV). This structure agrees closely with the structure of isolated dictyosomes and probably represents the form of dictyosomes in active cells. ×140,000. Photograph courtesy of Dr. D. Branton of the Department of Botany, University of California, Berkeley.

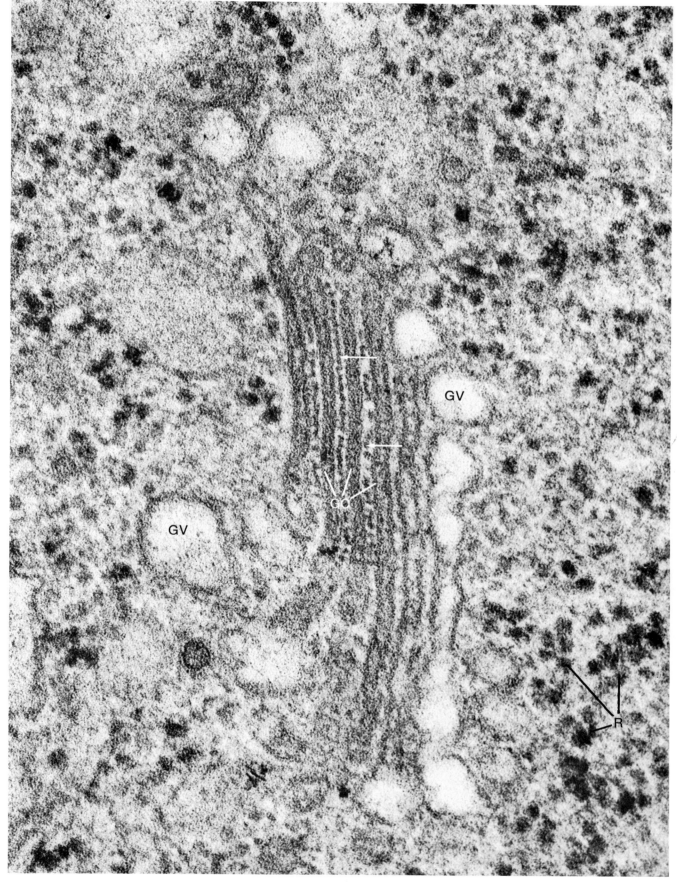

29

FIG. 6–4. High resolution photograph of a dictyosome from a corn root. Note the intercisternal tubular structures (arrows) present between the stacks of cisternae (GC). Vesicles (GV) are common and numerous ribosomes (R) are present. Tissue fixed in gluteraldehyde-osmium and stained with lead. ×235,000. Photograph courtesy of Dr. Hilton Mollenhauer, Kettering Foundation.

7   Nucleus and Endoplasmic Reticulum

The nucleus was first recognized as a universal cell part by Robert Brown in 1833. Since then, the nucleus has been the focus for research which attempts to explain the hereditary processes of the cell.

The nucleus is a relatively large structure (Fig. 7–1) found in all eucoryotic plant and animal cells at some stage of their development. The nucleus is surrounded by a membrane which, when viewed with the electron microscope, can be seen to consist of two membranes (Fig. 7–1). There are numerous pores that pierce these membranes and appear to connect the inside of the nucleus to the cytoplasm (Fig. 7–2). In a freeze-etched view of the nucleus, the pores can be seen quite readily and appear to be open (Fig. 7–2).

The interior of the nucleus contains a roughly spherical structure, the *nucleolus* (Fig. 7–3). The nucleolus was first discovered by Schleiden, who, with Schwann, is usually credited with the formulation of the cell theory. Under the light microscope the nucleolus is seen to consist of two phases. The first, a more solid densely stained phase, gives the general form to the structure. The second phase, much lighter and more liquid in appearance, is distributed throughout the solid phase. The electron microscope reveals that the more dense phase of the nucleolus consists of groups of particles (Fig. 7–3) which are the same size as ribosomes and contain RNA; others appear smaller in diameter and may consist of protein. The nucleolus also contains long fibrous strands of presumably proteinacious material which may func-tion as a structural element. Small granules are abundant in the lighter, more liquid areas.

The remainder of the nucleus is occupied by chromatin and the nuclear sap. Chromatin consists of the expanded chromosomes and is made up of DNA and protein. At mitosis or meiosis the chromatin condenses and the chromosomes are seen as discrete bodies within the nucleus. A great amount of genetical and biochemical data indicates that the DNA of the chromosomes is the hereditary material of the cell. (See J. Watson, *Molecular Biology of the Gene.*)

In the cytoplasm the ribosomes are frequently associated with long sheets of membrane called *endoplasmic reticulum* (ER) (Fig. 7–4). The endoplasmic reticulum gives rise to the nuclear membrane during mitosis (Chapter 9) and, in fact, the endoplasmic reticulum and the nuclear membrane may constitute one continuous membrane system throughout the cell. The endoplasmic reticulum which does not have ribosomes associated with it is called smooth ER. Endoplasmic reticulum with ribosomes is called rough ER.

The endoplasmic reticulum, both rough and smooth, seems to function as a transportation and storage system within the cell. It is believed that, in some cases, the endoplasmic reticulum is continuous with the plasma membrane and, thus, provides a canal for materials to enter the interior of the cell. In some cells the endoplasmic reticulum accumulates large masses of protein. In addition, a variety of other kinds of materials may be found within its interior. ●

SUGGESTED READINGS

GENERAL

ALLFREY, V. G., AND A. E. MIRSKY. "How Cells Make Molecules." *Scientific American,* September 1961. An excellent brief summary of DNA controlled protein synthesis in the cell.

NIRENBERG, M. W. "The Genetic Code: II." *Scientific American,* March 1963. A short paper covering the methods of translating genetic information into specific proteins.

WATSON, J. D. *Molecular Biology of the Gene.* New York: W. A. Benjamin, Inc., 1965. An excellent account of molecular biology by one of the founders of the field.

TECHNICAL

MIRSKY, A. E., AND S. OSAWA. "The Interphase Nucleus." In J. Brachet and A. E. Mirsky, eds., *The Cell* (New York: Academic Press, Inc., 1959–1964), Vol. 2, pp. 193–290.

PALADE, G. E. "Endoplasmic Reticulum." *J. Biophysical and Biochemical Cytology,* Supplement 2 (1956), p. 85.

PORTER, K. R. "The Ground Substance: Observations from Electron Microscopy." In J. Brachet and A. E. Mirsky, eds., *The Cell* (New York: Academic Press, Inc., 1959–1964), Vol. 2, p. 621.

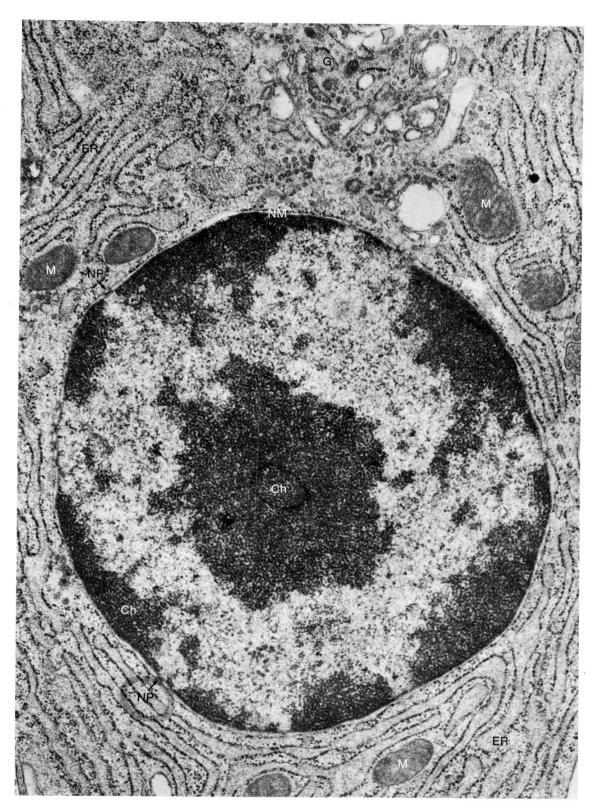

FIG. 7–1. Nucleus in a plasma cell of the guinea pig. This nucleus occupies a large portion of the cell, and the chromatin (Ch) is particularly evident as a mass of dark material. The nuclear membrane (NM) is obviously double, and nuclear pores (NP) are common. This cell is particularly rich in endoplasmic reticulum (ER). The surface of the ER is covered with ribosomes. Mitochondria (M) with numerous cristae are present. A Golgi complex (G) is visible near the nucleus. The cell has all the obvious features of a high metabolic activity. (For another example of a nucleus, see Fig. A–1 in the Appendix. In this nucleus, the chromatin is more uniformly dispersed in the cell and the nucleolus is prominent.) Gluteraldehyde-osmium fixation. ×30,000. Photograph courtesy of Dr. Donald Fawcett, Harvard Medical School.

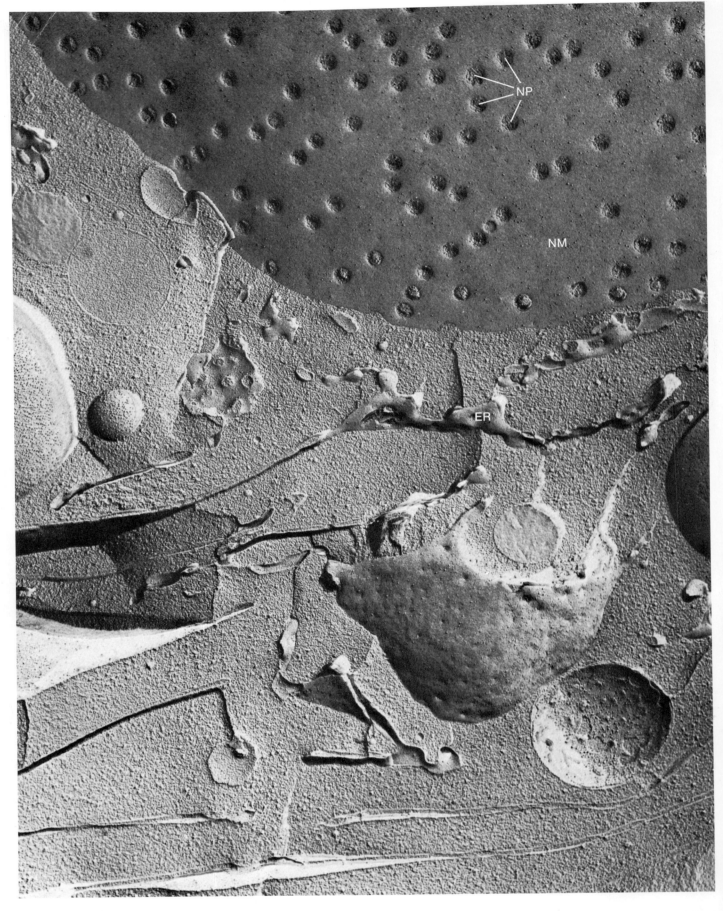

32

FIG. 7–2. Freeze-etch view of nucleus in an onion root tip cell. In this face view of the nuclear membrane (NM), the pores (NP) are particularly evident. Through the pores the interior of the nucleus can be seen. Pieces of the endoplasmic reticulum closest to the nucleus resemble the nuclear membrane in appearance while those more distant are continuous membranes. ×40,000.

That there are no ribosomes on the membranes of the nucleus and ER is explained on the basis of membrane splitting proposed by Branton (see Appendix). Photograph courtesy of Dr. D. Branton, University of California, Berkeley.

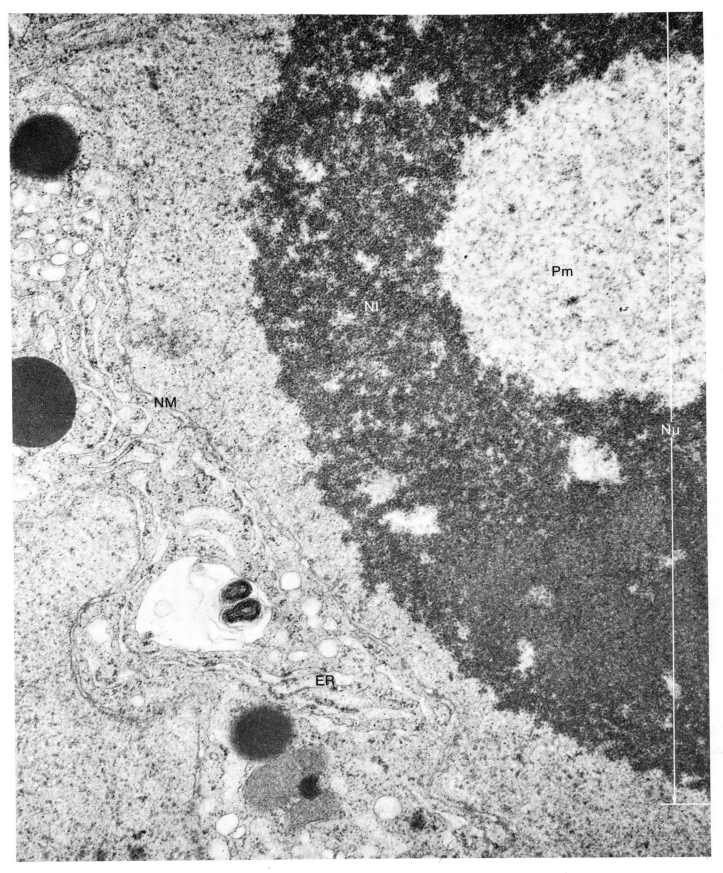

33

FIG. 7–3. Nucleolus of a polar nucleus of cotton. The two phases of the nucleolus (Nu) are evident. The darker is the nucleolemma (Nl) and the lighter is the pars mor-pha (Pm). The nucleolemma can be seen to be composed of small ribosome-like particles with the suggestion of filamentous material. Little of the nucleus can be seen. The nuclear membrane (NM) has many pores. Endoplasmic reticulum (ER) is seen in the cytoplasm. Tissue fixed in gluteraldehyde-osmium. Photograph, Dr. W. A. Jensen.

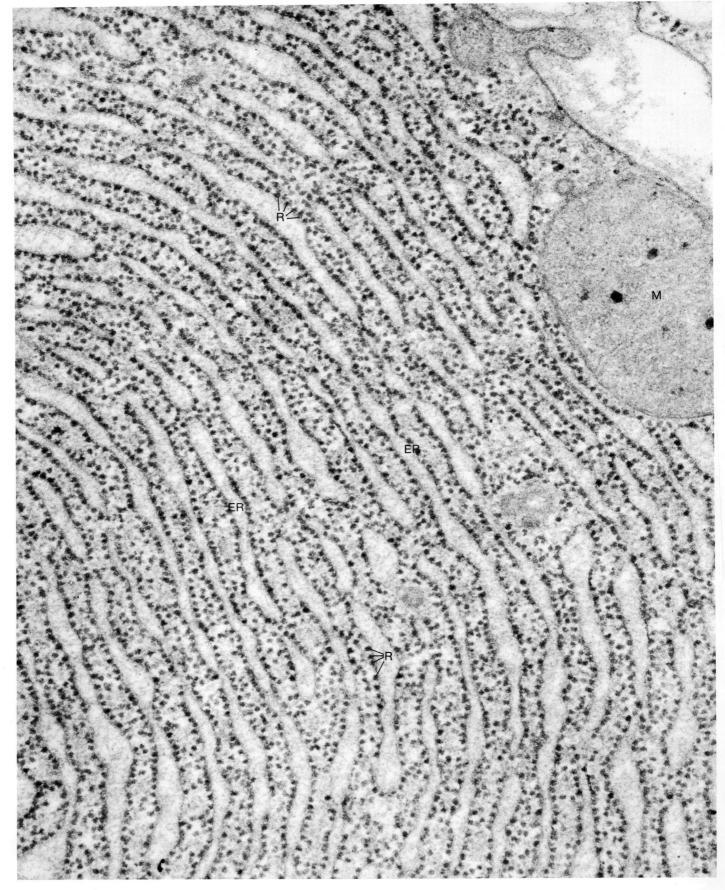

34

FIG. 7–4. Endoplasmic reticulum (ER) and ribosomes (R) in an exocrine cell of rat pancreas. The ribosomes are both associated with the ER and are free. This amount of ER and ribosomes is typical of cells rapidly synthesizing protein, particularly for excretion. A poorly fixed mitochondria (M) is also present. ×66,000. For a surface view of the ribosomes on the ER see Fig. 7–1.

Dr. George Palade supplied the photograph. Dr. Palade and his colleagues have long been associated with work on the ribosomes. He first described them in tissue sections, and for years they were known to many as Palade's particles.

8　Ribosomes

In all cells ribosomes are the site of protein synthesis from amino acids (see Fig. 8–1). In the early 1940s Brachet and Casperson suggested this when they showed that high rates of protein synthesis are associated with cells containing large amounts of RNA. It was found by centrifugal fractionation of cell homogenates that most of this RNA was bound to particles considerably smaller than mitochondria. When radioactive amino acids were fed to cells they first appeared bound in the ribosome fraction. This indicated that ribosomes were involved in some of the initial stages of protein synthesis. The ribosomes isolated in these early studies were not pure, but were attached to fragments of endoplasmic reticulum of the cell. This impure fraction consisting of ribosomes with endoplasmic reticulum is called the *microsomal fraction*.

We now know that ribosomes are but one of the required components necessary for the synthesis of protein. The others are messenger RNA, which carries the genetic message; soluble RNA, which carries the amino acids to be synthesized; and guanosine triphosphate, the source of energy. A number of ribosomes may be attached to the same messenger, each ribosome manufacturing its own chain of polypeptide. This structure, shown in Fig. 8–2, is called a *polysome*.

The site of the ribosomes within the cells was first demonstrated in thin sections of osmium fixed tissue. Examined with the electron microscope, these particles appear to be 170 to 230 A in diameter and are distributed along the endoplasmic reticulum of the cell, along the cell and nuclear membranes, and in the nucleus. Ribosomes may also exist free in the cytoplasm, as shown in Fig. 1–1 (top) and 4–5. Further observations have shown that there are two main classes of ribosomes, the smaller being found in procaryotic cells and the larger in eucaryotic cells. The ribosome itself consists of two sub-units, each one about 40 percent protein and 60 percent RNA by weight. To function actively in protein synthesis they must be bound into a complete ribosome. These subunits are easily visible in negatively stained *E. coli* ribosomes (see Fig. 8–1).

Though eucaryotic cells have the larger ribosome, procaryotic-like ribosomes are occasionally evident in preparations of eucaryotic cells. For example, a homogenate of higher plant leaves will demonstrate the presence of both kinds of ribosomes. It can be further shown that the procaryotic-like ribosomes originate from the chloroplast while the eucaryotic ribosomes come from the remainder of the cell.

The function of the large amount of RNA in the ribosome is still not known. The ribosomal RNA does not carry the genetic message which is translated into protein structure and it does not bind specific amino acids, for they are bound by the soluble RNA. Generally, nature is a conservative architect; it eliminates useless elaborations through the evolutionary process. It may be that this RNA functions as a code for some of the ribosomal protein.

●

SUGGESTED READINGS

GENERAL

RICH, A. "Polyribosomes." *Scientific American*, December 1963. A brief summary of recent information on ribosome function.

WATSON, J. D. "Involvement of RNA in the Synthesis of Proteins." *Science*, Vol. 140 (1963), pp. 17–26. An excellent summary of the mechanics of protein synthesis.

TECHNICAL

BONNETT, H. T., JR., AND E. H. NEWCOMB. "Polyribosomes and Cisternal Accumulations in Root Cells of Radish." *J. Cell Biol.*, Vol. 27 (1965), pp. 423–432.

HUXLEY, H. E., AND G. ZUBAY. "Electron Microscope Observations on the Structure of Microsomal Particles from *Escherichia coli*." *J. Mole. Biol.*, Vol. 2 (1960), pp. 10–18.

PALADE, G. E. "A Small Particulate Component of the Cytoplasm." *J. Biophysical and Biochemical Cytology*, Vol. 1 (1955), pp. 59–66. A classic paper in the history of ribosome research.

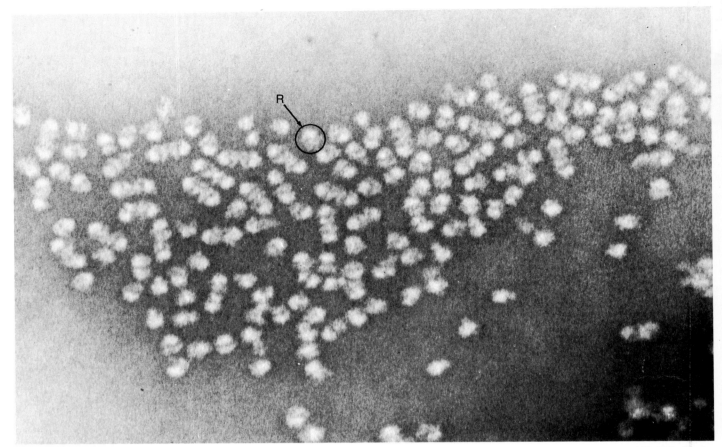

FIG. 8–1. Negatively stained ribosomes isolated from the bacterium *Escherichia coli*. Ribosomes containing two subunits (R) are active in protein synthesis. These subunits possess similar chemical composition and are bound together ionically through Mg++ ions. In many cases the active ribosomes are again joined through Mg++ ions to give particles containing four subunits. ×300,000. Photograph courtesy of Dr. H. E. Huxley, Cambridge University.

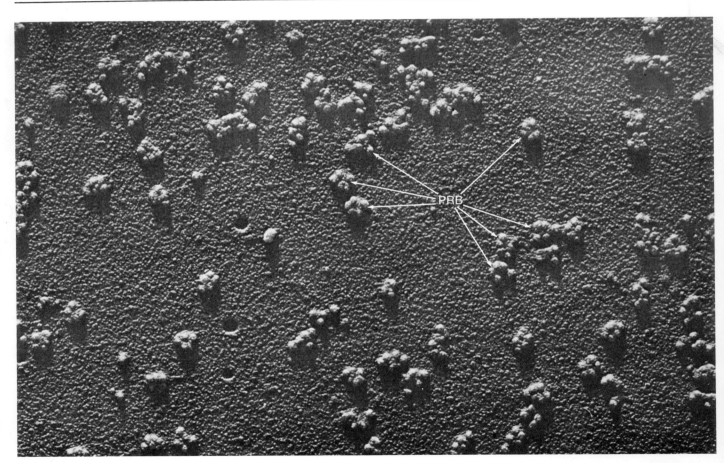

FIG. 8–2. A heavy metal shadowed preparation showing five and more rabbit reticulocyte ribosomes attached to one messenger RNA molecule to yield a polyribosome (PRB). These structures can be produced *in vitro* by mixing appropriate concentrations of messenger RNA and ribosomes. They also occur *in vivo*, as shown in Fig. 8–3. ×150,-000. Photograph courtesy of Dr. A. Rich, Massachusetts Institute of Technology.

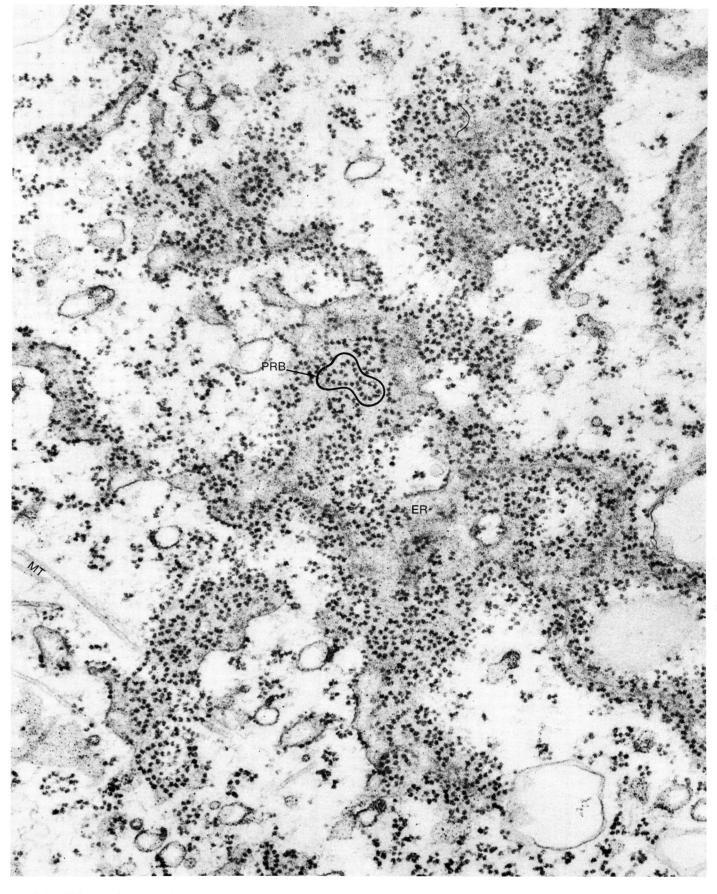

FIG. 8–3. Thin section of plant tissue (epidermal cell of radish root) showing ribosomal distributions on the surface of endoplasmic reticulum (ER). The linear distribution of ribosomes suggests very strongly that these ribosomes are bound together by messenger RNA to yield a polyribosome (PRB). Microtubules (MT) are also evident in the micrograph. Tissue fixed in gluteraldehyde-osmium and stained with lead. (Other sectional views of ribosomes are shown in Fig. 7–3.) ×59,000. Photograph courtesy of Dr. Eldon Newcomb, University of Wisconsin, and Dr. Howard Bonnett, University of Oregon.

9   Chromosomes and Cell Division

One of the first signs of cell division is a series of changes which occur within the nucleus. The process which results in the formation of two daughter nuclei is called *mitosis*. As the chromatin, which has been scattered throughout the matrix of the nucleus, condenses, the chromosomes are seen as distinct bodies containing a constricted portion called the *centromere*.

In most plant cells, while the chromosomes are condensing (Fig. 9–1), a clear zone develops around the outer edge of the nuclear membrane. As this clear zone reaches its maximal size and the chromosomes are fully condensed, the nuclear membrane disappears and the nucleolus dissolves. The centromeres then become aligned on a plane perpendicular to the axis of the division and midway between the two poles of the nucleus. Numerous fibers appear which are attached at one end to the centromeres (Fig. 9–2) and at the other to the poles, thus forming the spindle. Other fibers run directly from pole to pole. These fibers are believed to be formed from the protein which was accumulated in the clear zone before the nuclear membrane dissolved. In the next stage of mitosis, the centromeres divide and chromosomes separate longitudinally into two new chromosomes. The centromeres then move toward the poles of the spindle apparatus and the arms of the chromosomes appear to be pulled to the poles (Fig. 9–3). When the separated chromosomes have completed their migration to the poles, a nuclear membrane begins to form around each chromosome mass. The endoplasmic reticulum appears to be the source of these new nuclear membrane (Fig. 9–4).

In plant cells, the spindle fibers appear to persist at the midpoint of the two separated chromosome masses. Small vesicles accumulate in this region and fuse into a plate. This is the initial stage in the formation of the new cell wall. This plate forms first in the region of the original spindle and then additional fibers appear which extend the plate toward the original walls. Eventually, the plate fuses with the walls. The fusion of these vesicles gives rise to both the new cell wall and the new cell membrane.

In the case of animal cells and some plant cells, two distinct bodies called *centrioles* (Fig. 9–5) are associated with the nucleus. Each centriole is a cylinder of material composed of nine bundles of three microtubules. These divide and two centrioles migrate to each pole of the nucleus.

The spindle apparatus is usually much more complicated in animals than in plants. In animal cells, the centrioles become the center of organization of the spindle apparatus. Spindle fibers radiate in all directions from the centrioles, both toward the chromosomes and into the cytoplasm. Also, in animal cells, the plasma membrane invaginates toward the mid-region of the spindle apparatus. Eventually, the plasma membranes from the opposite sides of the cell fuse and two cells are separated (see Fig. 9–6).

The microtubules which form the spindle fibers are also found in other parts of both animal and plant cells (see Chapter 10). ●

SUGGESTED READINGS

GENERAL

MAZIA, D. "How Cells Divide." *Scientific American,* September 1961, pp. 100–108. An excellent summary of mitosis, including good electron microscope photographs.

MAZIA, D. "Mitosis and the Physiology of Cell Division." In J. Brachet and A. E. Mirsky, eds., *The Cell* (New York: Academic Press, Inc., 1959–1964), Vol. 3, p. 77. A masterful summary of our knowledge of mitosis in animals and plants.

TECHNICAL

MOSES, M. J., AND J. R. COLMAN. "Structural Patterns and Functional Organization of Chromosomes." In M. Locke, ed., *The Role of Chromosomes in Development,* 23rd Growth Symposium, 1964.

STERN, H. "Function and Reproduction of Chromosomes." *Physiological Reviews,* Vol. 42, 1962.

WHALEY, W. G., M. DAUWALDER, AND J. E. KEPHART. "The Golgi Apparatus and an Early Stage in Cell Plate Formation." *J. Ultrastructural Research,* Vol. 15 (1966), pp. 169–180.

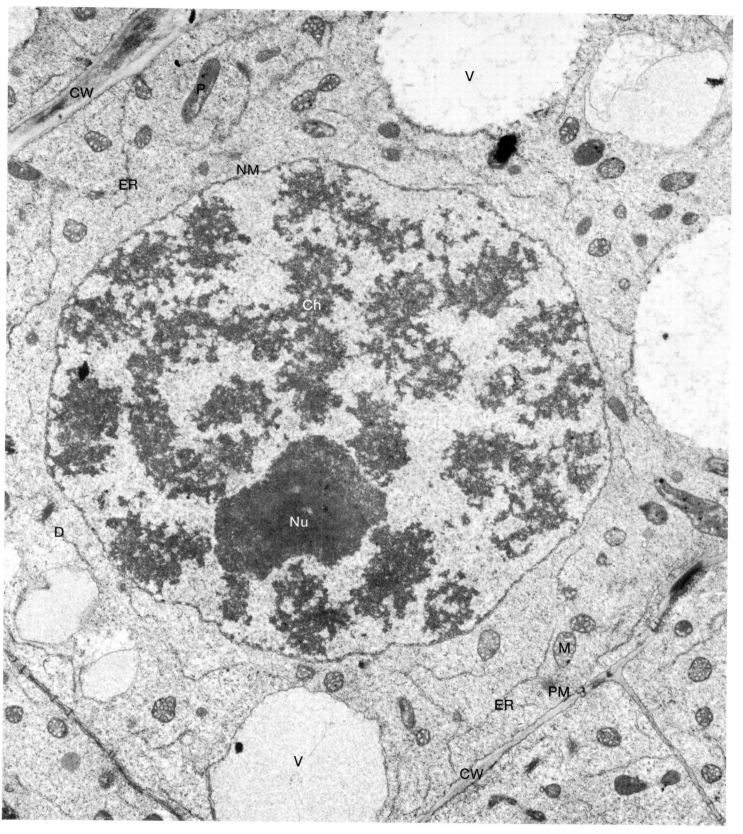

FIG. 9–1. Prophase in a meristematic cell of the onion root tip. The chromosomes (Ch) are condensing and are clearly visible. The nucleolus (Nu) is irregular in shape and will shortly disappear. The nucleus is still surrounded by the nuclear membrane (NM), although it will break down at the end of pro-phase. Relatively small vacuoles (V) are present in the cell. Mitochondria (M), plastids (P), endoplasmic reticulum (ER), dictyosomes (D), plasma membrane (PM), and cell wall (CW) can be seen in the cell. Note the absence of any cell parts immediately adjacent to the nuclear membrane. Tissue fixed in gluteraldehyde-osmium and stained with uranium and lead. Compare this nucleus with that of interphase nucleus from the same tissue in Appendix. ×12,000. Photograph, Dr. W. A. Jensen.

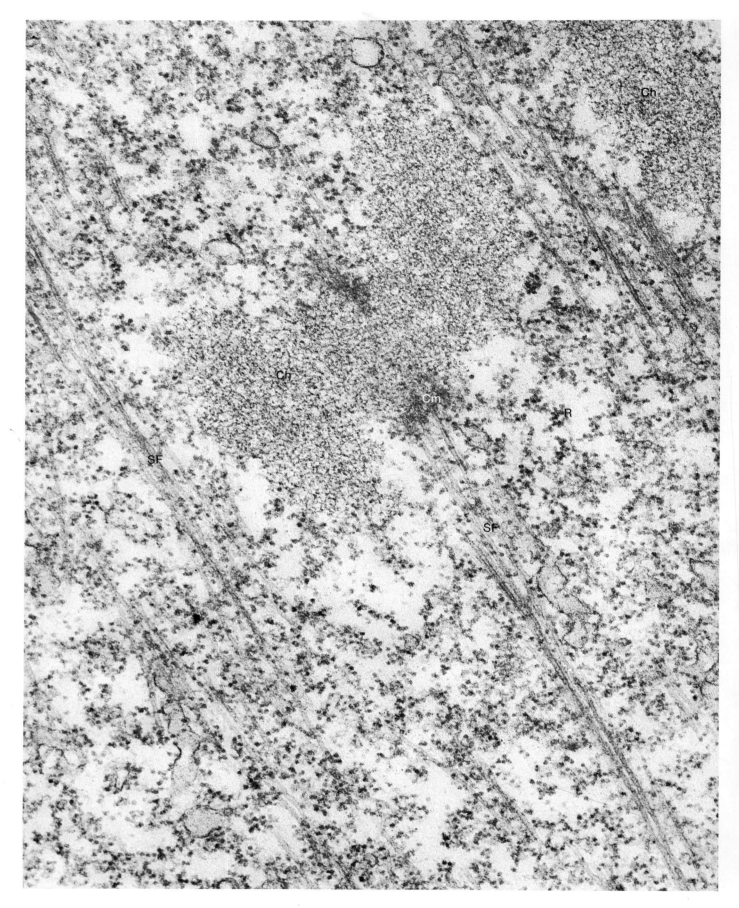

FIG. 9–2. Spindle fibers (SF) attached to chromosome (Ch) at the centromere (Cm). This is the prometaphase stage of the first division of the sea urchin embryo. The spindle fibers are very similar to the microtubules discussed in Chapter 10. The tissue was fixed in osmium in a 0.5 sodium acetate buffer at pH 6.1 and stained with lead hydroxide. ×70,000. Photograph courtesy of Dr. Patricia Harris, Oregon State University.

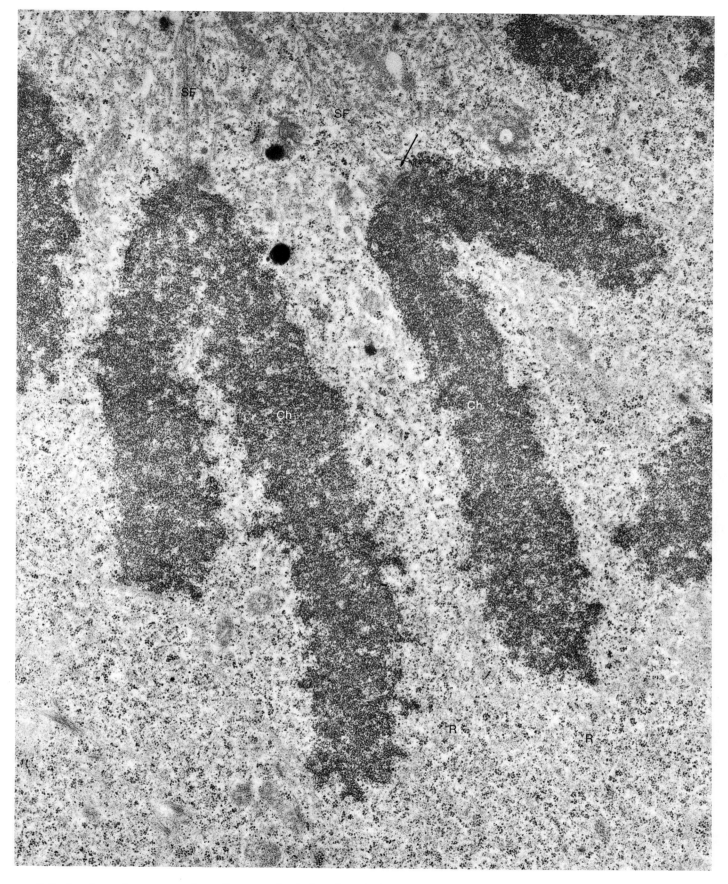

FIG. 9–3. Anaphase chromosomes from the Tasmanian Wallaby. The structure of the chromosomes (Ch) is particularly clear. The point of attachment of the spindle fibers (SF) can be seen at the centromere or kinetochore (arrow). Ribosomes (R) are plentiful. Tissue fixed in gluteraldehyde-osmium and stained with uranium and lead. ×24,000. Photograph courtesy of Dr. B. R. Brinkley, M.D. Anderson Hospital, University of Texas.

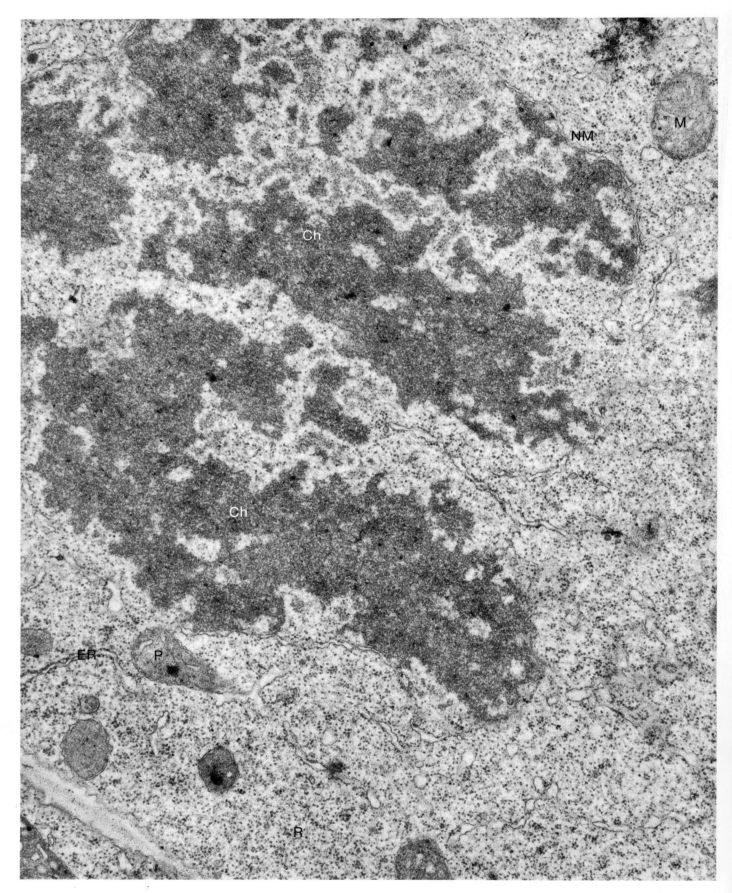

42

FIG. 9–4. Late telephase in an onion root tip cell. The chromosomes (Ch) are expanding and the nuclear membrane (NM) is beginning to form from the endoplasmic reticulum (ER). The formation of the nuclear membranes is not yet complete, and there is essentially no difference between the ground substance associated with the chromosomes and that which will be outside the nuclear membrane when it is complete. Mitochondria (M) and plastids (P) are present, as are numerous ribosomes (R). Tissue was fixed in gluteraldehyde-osmium and stained with uranium and lead. ×71,000. Photograph courtesy of Mrs. Paula Stetler, University of California, Berkeley.

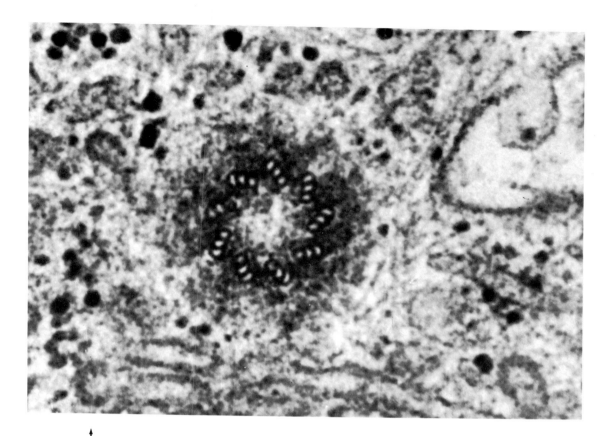

43

FIG. 9–5. Cross and longitudinal views of the centrioles from Chinese hamster fibroblast cells. The arrangement of the microtubules composing the centrioles are similar to those found in the flagella. The centriole is a far from simple structure, and its role in cell division is an important one. Tissue fixed in gluteraldehyde-osmium and stained with lead and uranium. Top, ×132,000; bottom, ×110,000. Photograph courtesy of Dr. Elton Stubblefield, M. D. Anderson Hospital, University of Texas.

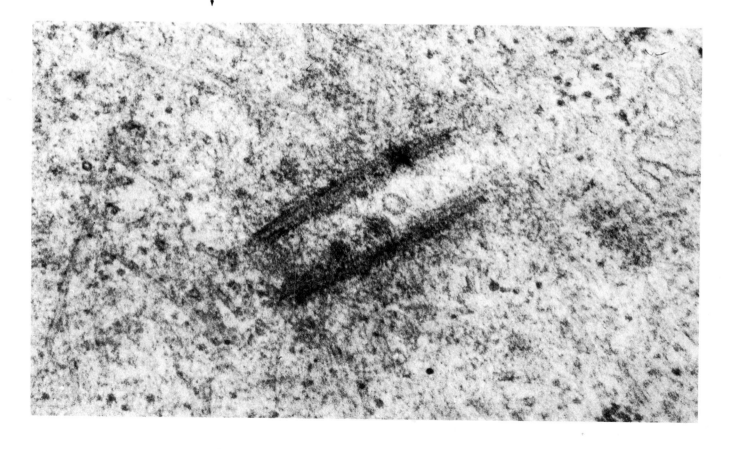

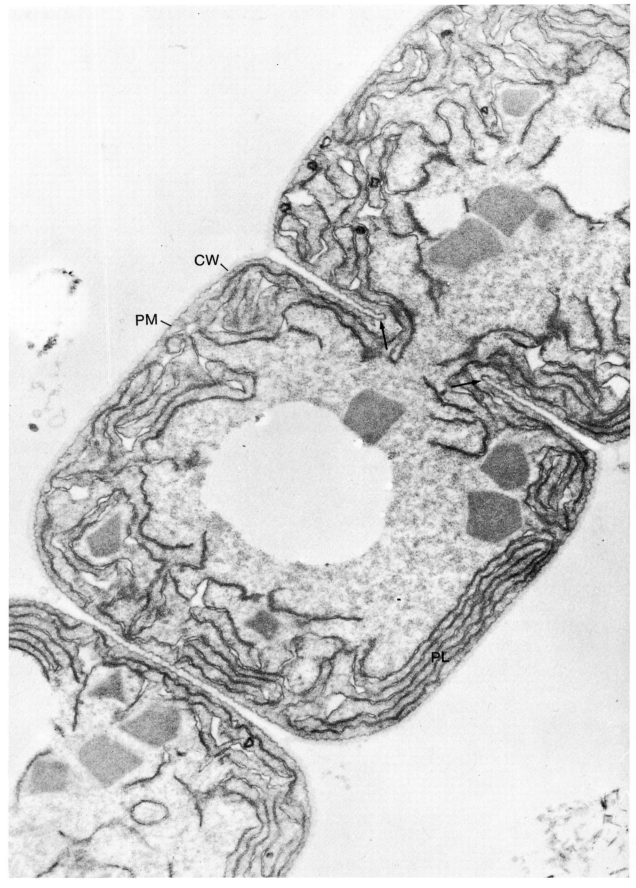

44

FIG. 9–6. Cell division in a procaryotic cell occurs by the formation of a new cell wall which starts at the edge of the cell and proceeds inward until the two cells are completely separate. This type of cell division is shown in *Anabaena*, a blue-green alga. The cell wall (CW) and plasma membrane (PM) are seen extending into the cell (arrows) and will eventually meet and result in a continuous wall, such as exists at lower end of cell. The membranes (PL) which contain both the photosynthetic and respiratory functions are seen clearly in this photograph. The cells were fixed in KMnO₄, which reveals the membranes but which removes the ribosomes and some other cell parts. Compare this preparation with Fig. 1–2 in which another blue-green alga has been fixed in gluteraldehyde-osmium. ×30,000. Photograph courtesy of Dr. Norma Lang, University of California, Davis.

10   Microtubules and Flagella

The 230–270 A diameter microtubules present in mitotic spindles are also found in many other regions of eucaryotic cells. For example, they are particularly abundant adjacent to the plasma membrane of higher plant cells (Fig. 10–1) and may participate in protoplasmic streaming. Microtubules are also abundant in many animal cells, such as the two concentric circles of microtubules in suctorian tentacles. These may be responsible for moving the digesting enzymes up the outside of the tentacle and to the prey, and, simultaneously, moving the digested material down the center of the tentacle.

Figure 10–1 (insert) shows, in cross section, the fine structure of a microtubule, which consists of 13 filaments radially arranged on 45 A centers. The microtubule is remarkable for its structural similarity to a subunit of the flagellum of eucaryotic cells. These flagella (Fig. 10–2) are generally 0.15–0.3 microns in diameter and 5–150 microns in length. They are surrounded by the plasma membrane, within which is a ring of nine double fibrils enclosing two central fibrils. The tails extending from the peripheral double fibrils characteristically face clockwise when viewed from the basal toward the distal end. These tails appear to contain the ATPase activity of

the flagellum and are, therefore, implicated in flagellar motion. Flagella are composed of 20 percent lipid and 60–70 percent protein.

The eucaryotic flagellum is associated in the cell interior with a basal body (Fig. 10–3) similar in structure to the centriole described in Chapter 9. In the basal body the tails of the nine peripheral fibrils are closed and give the appearance of three adjacent microtubules. Arising from the basal body are fine fibrils, which converge into a bundle frequently ending near the nucleus.

Bacterial flagella, only 100–350 A in diameter, are much smaller than eucaryotic flagella. The bacterial flagellum consists of three to ten parallel or helically intertwined filaments which are often composed of 45 A diameter subunits. Though the number of filaments varies with the bacterium studied, all bacterial flagella bear an obvious resemblance to the microtubule.

The exact molecular mechanism of eucaryotic flagellar motion has yet to be determined. In addition, it still isn't certain that bacteria flagella are motile organs which are independent of body motions. The many complex types of flagellar motion indicate that the final solution to these problems may elude us for some time. ●

SUGGESTED READINGS

GENERAL

HAYASHI, T. "How Cells Move." *Scientific American,* September 1961. A general discussion of cilia, flagella, and cell movement.

SATIR, P. "Cilia." *Scientific American,* February 1961. A good elementary introduction to cilia and flagella.

TECHNICAL

HOLWILL, M. E. J. "Physical Aspects of Flagellar Movement." *Physiological Reviews,* Vol. 46 (1966), pp. 696–785.

LEDBETTER, M. C., AND K. R. PORTER. "Morphology of Microtubular of Plant Cells." *Science,* Vol. 144 (1964), pp. 872–874. A classic article on the ultrastructure of the microtubules.

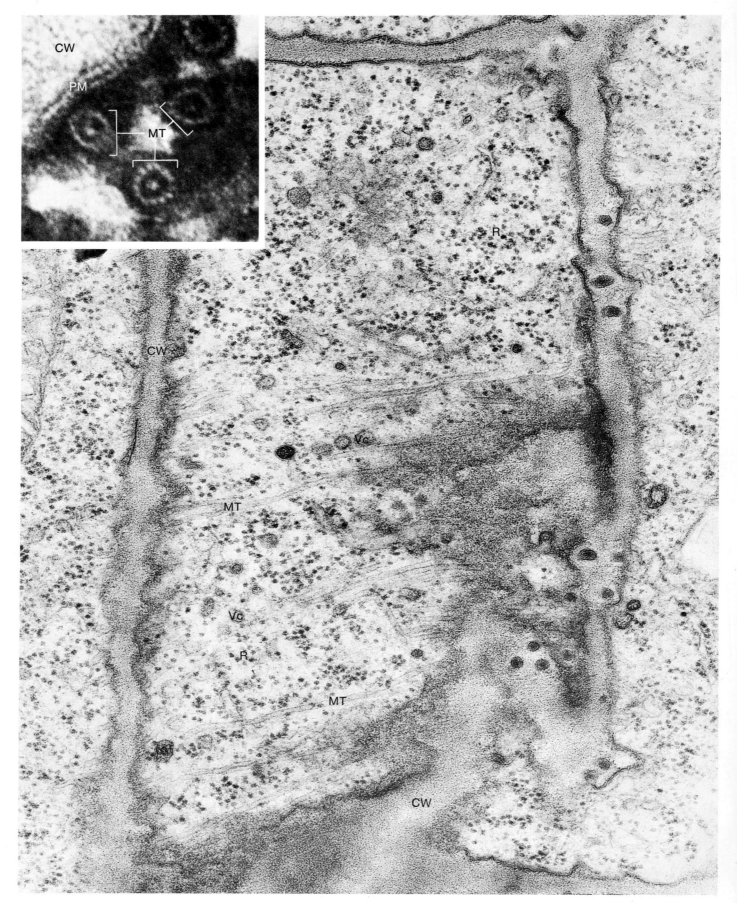

46

FIG. 10–1. Microtubules in a young, enlarging cell from root tip of bean (*Phaseolus vulgaris* L.). The section passes into the cell somewhat obliquely, showing a portion of a side wall in face view and microtubules (MT) lying in the cytoplasm just beneath the wall (CW). Vesicles (Vc) and ribosomes (R) are present around the microtubules. Tissue fixed in gluteraldehyde-osmium. ×70,000. Courtesy of Dr. E. H. Newcomb, University of Wisconsin.

INSERT: Sections of microtubules from the root tip of *Juniperus chinensis*. The substructure of the microtubules can be readily seen. There are 13 subunits in a ring around the core of the microtubule. The intense dark color is natural in this tissue resulting in a "natural negative staining." ×52,000. Photograph courtesy of Dr. Myron Ledbetter, Brookhaven National Laboratory, Long Island, N. Y. Dr. Ledbetter, working with Dr. Porter at Harvard University, has been associated with much of the basic research on microtubules.

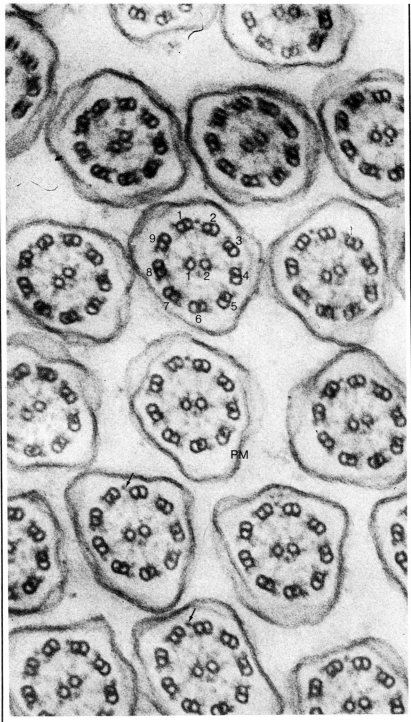

FIG. 10–2. Cross section of a lateral cilia from the gill of the freshwater mussel, *Elliptio complanatus*. The nine peripheral double fibrils and the two central single fibrils can be clearly seen. The tails extending from the peripheral double fibrils can be seen in some of the flagella (arrows). The fibrils are enclosed by a plasma membrane (PM). ×100,-000. Photograph courtesy of Dr. Peter Satir, University of Chicago.

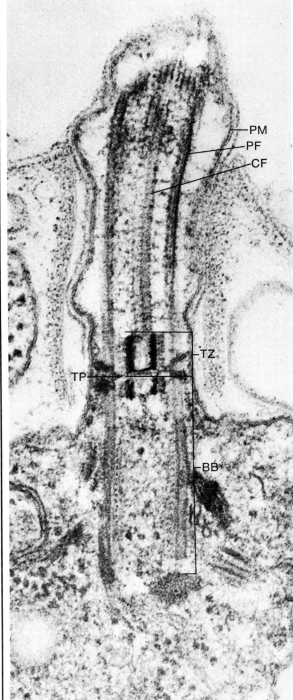

47

FIG. 10–3. Flagellum and basal body of the green unicellular alga, *Chlamydomonas*. The flagellum can be seen entering the cell at the top of the picture, the peripheral fibers (PF) and the central fibers (CF) being surrounded by the plasma membrane (PM). The central fibers end in the transition zone (TZ) in which the terminal plate (TP) can be seen. The basal body (BB) extends from the transition zone into the cell. The microfibrils connecting the basal body to the remainder of the cell cannot be seen in this preparation. Cell fixed in gluteraldehyde-osmium and stained with uranium and lead. ×92,000. Photograph courtesy of Dr. David Ringo, Yale University.

11   Extracellular Structures

Many cells secrete or precipitate substances which form protective or supporting structures outside the plasma membrane. Common examples of such extracellular structures are plant cell walls, bone, cartilage, and bacterial cell walls. All these structures are particularly suited for self-assembly and their production is controlled by adjacent cells. While the subunits of these structures are held together by covalent bonds, the structures themselves are held together by hydrogen bonds and Van der Waal's forces. The tensile strength of a piece of wood, or our own skin, is a result of these noncovalent forms of bonding.

Collagen, an extracellular substance of great importance, is a major component of skin, tendons, and bone and is produced mainly by fibroblast cells. Collagen is made up of proteins, called tropocollagens, of molecular weight 360,000 and which are about 2800 A long and 14 A in diameter. In the hands of a chemist, these subunits can precipitate out of acidic solution to form native collagen (Fig. 11–1). The collagen in this micrograph is made from a great many tropocollagen units which overlap for one-quarter of their length, as shown in Diagram 11–1. Thus, this highly differentiated extracellular structure has a great self-assembly power by virtue of the ease with which it crystallizes to form the collagen strand.

The 100 A–200 A diameter composite fibrils of plant cell walls, shown in Fig. 11–2, are another example of structures built of hydrogen-bonded subunits. The composite fibrils are made up from 45 A diameter elementary fibrils. These are composed of sugar polymers, which in some plants consist almost entirely of cellulose. This structure is shown in Diagram 11–2. In such cellulose elementary fibrils cellulose molecules, each of which may be up to microns in length, are stretched along the length of the fibril. These molecules are held together by hydrogen bonds and in some regions of the fibrils crystallize so as to yield a sharp X-ray diffraction pattern.

Most elementary fibrils contain other sugars beside glucose in the noncrystalline regions. The elementary fibrils are usually embedded in a noncellulosic polysaccharide matrix, as, for instance, reinforcing rods are embedded in concrete. This structure comprises the primary plant cell wall. An interesting facet of developmental biology concerns the role of these structures in cell elongation. Roelofson's theory of multinet growth states that the microfibrils are initially laid down perpendicular to the axis of elongation. By the time they have been forced to the outside of the wall they have assumed an orientation parallel to the axis of elongation. This is beautifully shown in Fig. 11–2.

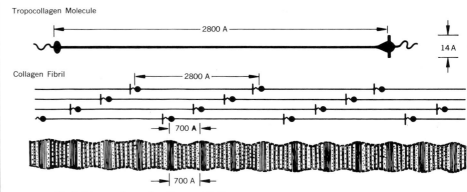

Tropocollagen Molecule
2800 A
14 A

Collagen Fibril
2800 A
700 A
700 A

DIAGRAM 11–1. Formation of collagen fibrils from tropocollagen molecules. Adapted from J. Gross, *Scientific American,* July 1961.

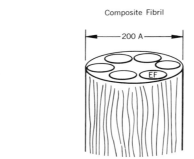

Composite Fibril
200 A
EF

DIAGRAM 11–2. Simplified representation of structure of the composite fibrils seen in Fig. 11–1.

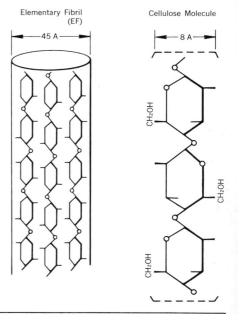

Elementary Fibril (EF)
45 A

Cellulose Molecule
8 A
CH₂OH

The cell walls of procaryotic cells are enormously complex structures which contain six or more layers when viewed in section by electron microscopy. They are built of protein and lipid held together by hydrogen bonding, Van der Waal's forces, and, probably, hydrophobic bonding. Such an array, viewed by negative staining, is shown in Fig. 11–3. While the enormous regularity of this wall appears startling, such structures can be formed quite spontaneously by a number of lipids. Bangham and Horne have observed that a mixture of lecithin, cholesterol, and saponin formed similar complex structures (see Fig. 11–4). This model structure is also held together by hydrogen bonding, Van der Waal's forces, and hydrophobic bonding.

These extracellular substances share with the viruses and membranes very great powers of self-assembly. This power reflects the unique crystallization properties inherent in the molecules of which they are composed.

Another fascinating example of an extracellular structure is the surface of the cutinaceous layer which lies over plant epidermal cells (Fig. 11–5). Wax is apparently pushed through the cutinaceous layer to the leaf surface, and this accounts for its shiny appearance. The morphology of these wax extrusions is apparently one way in which aphids distinguish among the various leaves. ●

SUGGESTED READINGS

GENERAL

FREY-WYSSLING, A., AND K. MÜHLETHALER. *Ultrastructural Plant Cytology.* New York: American Elsevier Publishing Company, 1965. A penetrating review of electron and light microscope studies of plant cells which includes extensive discussion of the cell wall.

GROSS, J. "Collagen." *Scientific American,* May, 1961, pp. 120–130. An excellent summary of the biochemistry and structure of collagen.

PRESTON, R. D. "Cellulose." *Scientific American,* September 1951. A brief summary of some of the basic concepts of the cellulose molecule and wall structure.

TECHNICAL

JUNIPER, B. E. "The Surfaces of Plants." *Endeavour,* Vol. 18 (1959), p. 20.

MURRAY, R. G. E. "On the Cell Wall Structure of *Spirillum serpens." Can. J. of Microbiol.* Vol. 9 (1963), p. 381.

ROELOFSON, P. A., AND A. L. HOUWINK. "Fibrillar Architecture of Growing Plant Cell Walls." *Acta Botanica Neerlandica,* Vol. 3 (1954), pp. 385–395.

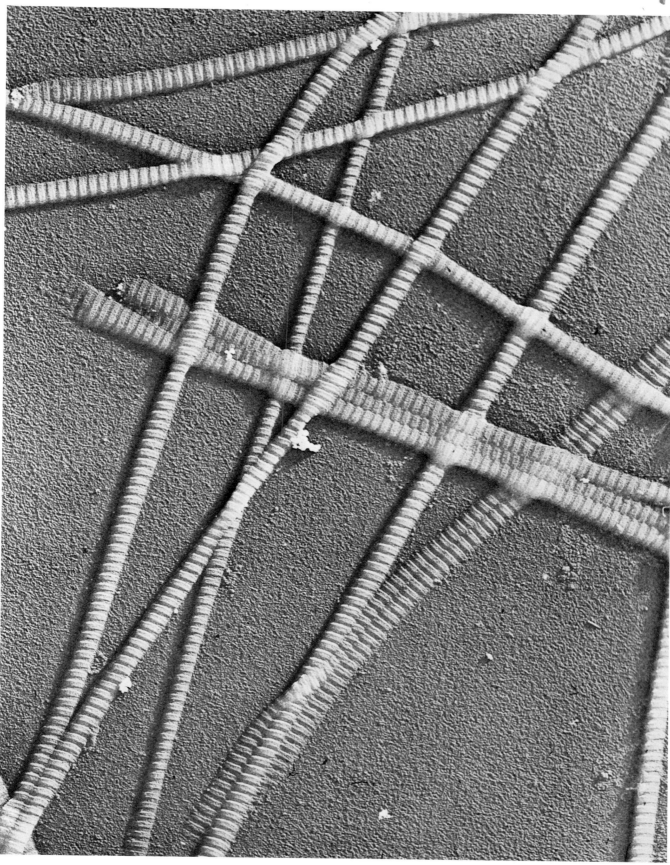

Fɪɢ. 11–1. Bovine skin collagen fibrils shadowed with chromium. Each fibril is made from many tropocollagen molecules as shown in Diagram 11–1. The tropocollagen molecules are bound together by hydrogen bonds. ×43,000. Photograph courtesy of J. Gross, Massachusetts Institute of Technology.

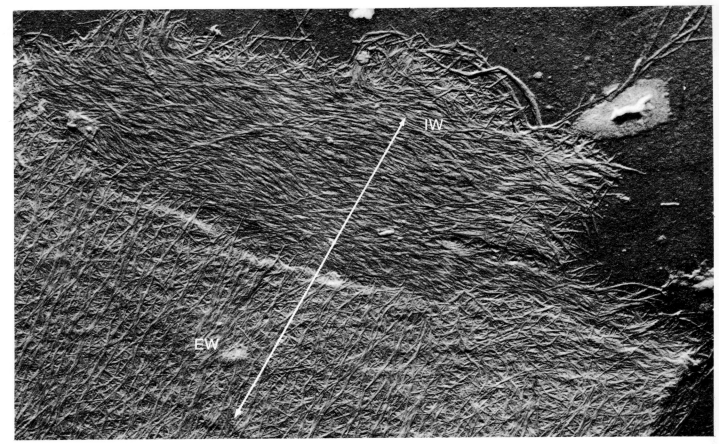

FIG. 11–2. A heavy metal shadowed preparation of a higher plant *(Juncus)* primary cell wall. Note that the composite fibrils on the interior of the wall (IW) are perpendicular to the long axis of the cell, microfibrils on the exterior of the wall (EW) are parallel to the long axis of the cell while those in between are intermediate in orientation. The direction of cell elongation is given by the large arrow. ×38,000. Photograph courtesy of Professor P. A. Roelofsen, Technische Hogeschool, Delft, Netherlands.

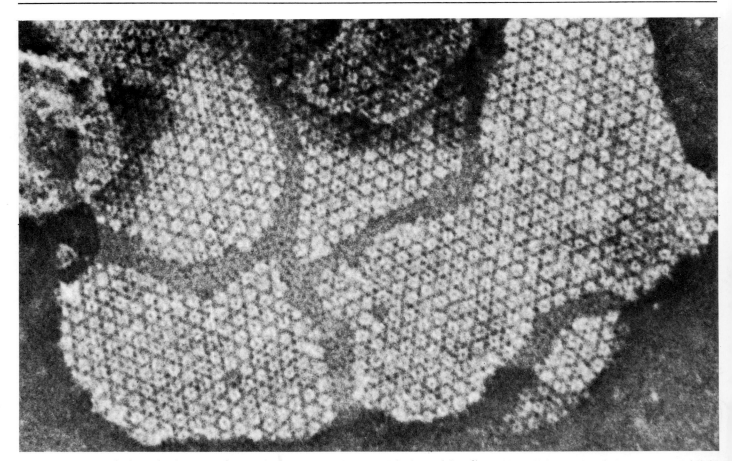

FIG. 11–3. A negatively stained preparation bacterial *(Spirillum serpens)* cell wall. This wall is built from smaller, more highly oriented subunits than the elementary cellulose fibrils shown in Fig. 11–2. The bacterial wall is mucopolysaccharide in character, a molecular association that would not supply the strength required in higher plant cell walls. This wall is closely mimicked by model lipid systems as shown in Fig. 11–4. ×300,000. Photograph courtesy of Dr. R. Murray, Univesity of Western Ontario.

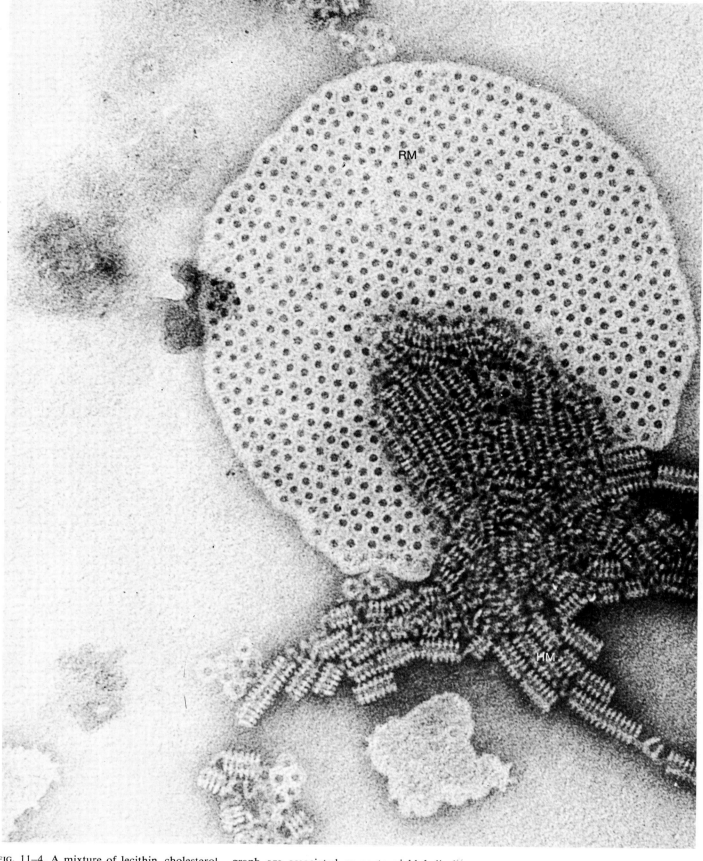

51

FIG. 11–4. A mixture of lecithin, cholesterol, and saponin viewed by negative staining. Two types of micellar patterns are evident. In the upper region of the picture the lipid molecules are arranged radially to yield radial micelles (RM), whereas the lipid molecules in the lower region of the micrograph are associated so as to yield helical micelles (HM). The degree of complexity in crystallization of these mixtures is an indication of how the complexity of bacterial cell wall structure might be explained. ×240,000. Photograph supplied by Drs. Bangham and Horne, Cambridge University.

FIG. 11–5. Surface replica of *Eucalyptus* leaf showing the configurations assumed by the wax exuded through the cutinaceous layer. ×9,200. Photograph supplied by Dr. B. Juniper, Oxford University.

12 Viruses

Viruses are infectious particles (Figs. 12–1, 12–2) containing RNA or DNA wrapped in a protein coat. The bacterial viruses, or phage, contain DNA whereas the animal and plant viruses generally contain RNA. The genetic information in these viruses is sufficient to produce more virus particles at the expense of a host cell. In bacteriophage, genetic information of the host may be also carried in the viral DNA.

Kleinschmidt has developed a beautiful technique for demonstrating the morphology of the DNA in a bacteriophage or cellular material. In this technique the phage particles are floated on diluted phosphate buffer as a film. The film is then picked up and subjected to heavy metal shadow casting on an electron microscope grid. Such a picture is shown in Fig. 12–1. It can be seen that the phage has burst and exuded a continuous strand of DNA. When the phage attacks a receptive bacterial cell, the coat remains outside the bacterial cell and the DNA is injected into the interior of the bacterium carrying its genetic message for the production of more phage protein and nucleic acid.

The first virus to be crystallized, tobacco mosaic virus, contains RNA. A shadowed preparation of TMV is shown in Fig. 12–2. This virus is up to three microns in length and about 170 A in diameter. It consists of a hollow central core surrounded by strands of RNA enclosed in protein subunits. When this virus is rubbed on a tobacco plant leaf, it enters the cells and may either cause spreading lesions in the leaf or a systemic infection throughout the plant.

Discussions as to whether viruses are living or non-living material are hindered by an assumption that there are only two categories of biological material. A virus might best be considered an agent which can express its activity only in the presence of living cells. In this sense, a virus is no more a living organism than is an isolated nucleus which also cannot continue to reproduce its genetic information and protein unless present in the cytoplasm of the eucaryotic cell. Viruses, rather than being the simplest expression of living things, may in fact be a relatively late evolutionary event and, thus, represent a sophisticated elaboration of life processes in a most specialized form.

●

SUGGESTED READINGS

GENERAL

JACOB, F., AND E. L. WOLLMAN. "Viruses and Genes." *Scientific American,* June 1961. A good introduction to the general study of viruses.

STENT, G. S. *Molecular Biology of Bacterial Viruses.* San Francisco: W. H. Freeman & Company, 1963. A well written book on those viruses which infect bacterial cells.

TECHNICAL

KLEINSCHMIDT, A. K., D. LANG, D. JACHERTS, AND R. K. ZAHN. "Darstellung und Längenmessungen des gesamten. Deoxyribonucleinsäure: Inhalts von T2 Bakteriophagen." *Biochem. Biophys. Acta,* Vol. 61 (1962), p. 857ff. This paper discusses the method of spreading viral DNA.

WILLIAMS, R. C. "The Shapes and Sizes of Purified Viruses as Determined by Electron Microscopy." *Cold Spring Harbor Symp. Quant. Biol.,* Vol. 18 (1953), p. 185. An excellent summary paper by one of the founders of the field of virus ultrastructure.

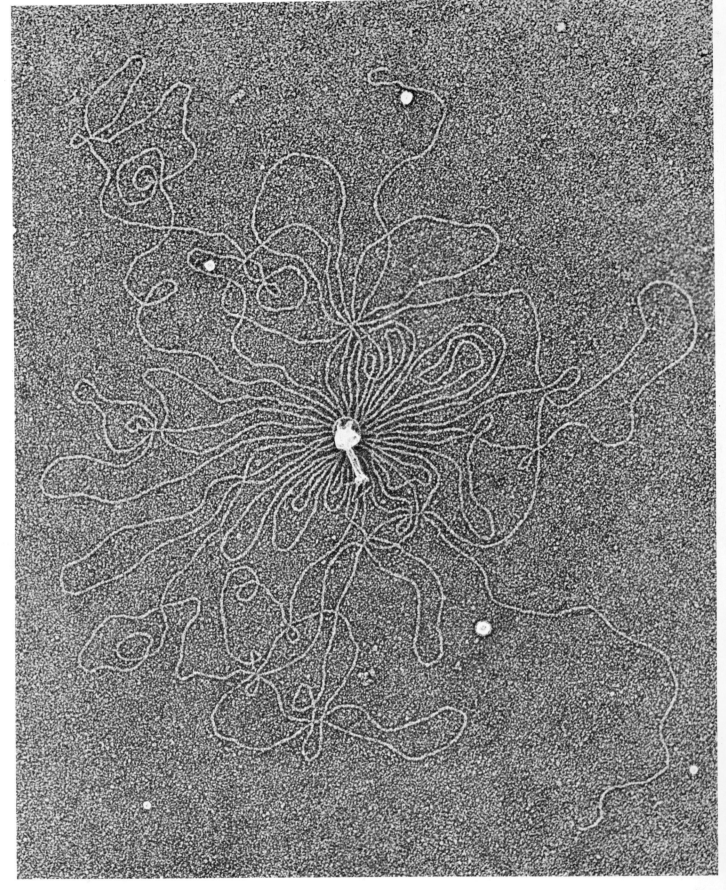

54

FIG. 12–1. An osmotically ruptured bacteriophage particle prepared by the Kleinschmidt technique. The protein coat of the phage is evident in the center of the micrograph while the DNA originally contained within it appears as a single continuous thread. The appearance the thread gives of being too large to fit inside the phage particle is due to the amplification of the width of the DNA double helix by the preparative procedure. The actual molecular diameter is only about one-tenth the length of that shown in the micrograph. ×95,000. Micrograph courtesy of Dr. Kleinschmidt, New York University Medical School.

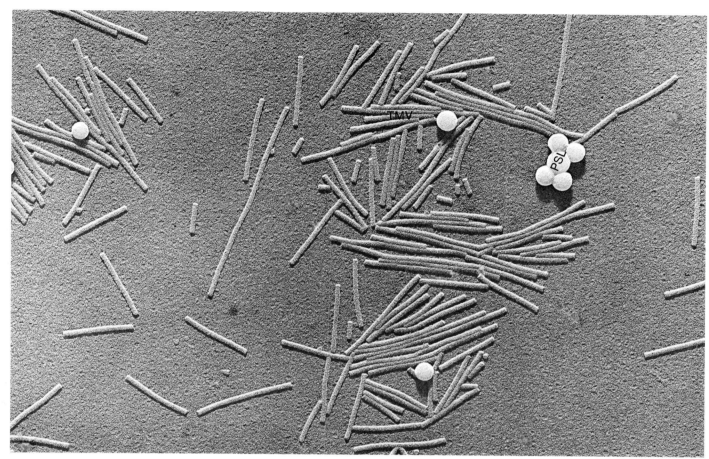

FIG. 12–2. Chromium shadowed tobacco mosaic virus (TMV) in the presence of 880 A Polystyrene (PSL) calibration spheres. The diameter of the TMV rods may be calibrated from relative shadow length of the PSL and TMV. ×52,000. Photograph, Dr. R. B. Park.

FIG. 12–3. Electron micrograph of a purified preparation of poliomyelitis virus, Type 2 (MEF–1). Dried from a water suspension and shadowed with uranium. Note the uniformity of particle size, leading to small regions of ordered array. This virus has been crystallized to form crystals about 0.2 mm. across. Poliovirus is an example of the size and shape shown by many RNA-containing viruses, both animal and plant, having an isometric shape and a diameter about 30 mμ. ×70,000. Photograph courtesy of Drs. C. E. Schewerdt and R. C. Williams, Virus Laboratory, University of California, Berkeley.

55

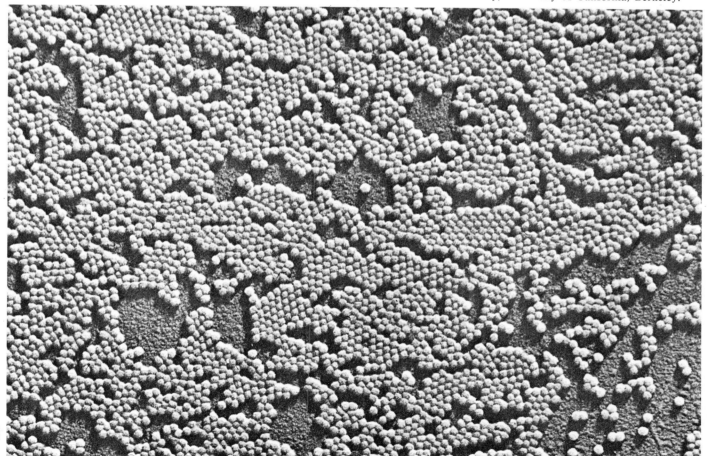

Appendix

The meaning of a light or electron micrograph is much enhanced if the viewer has some appreciation of the techniques and physical principles governing the formation of the image which is photographed. The similarities and differences between light microscopy and electron microscopy can be demonstrated by observing the same material with each microscope and comparing the results.

On the opposite page there are two micrographs of sectioned onion root. Each micrograph is at the same magnification ($\times$ 1000), but they differ in that the first micrograph was taken with the light microscope and the second with the electron microscope. One is struck by the amazing clarity or resolution of the electron micrograph as compared to the light micrograph.

A Comparison of the Light and the Electron Microscopes

The term resolution may be defined as that distance between two approaching objects at which the objects loose their unique and separate identity. At this point it is no longer possible to tell for certain whether one is observing one or two objects in the microscope. Thus if we say point to point resolution of the light microscope is 0.5 μ, we mean that two points of light, for example, which are closer together than 0.5 μ will appear as a single object. On the other hand, when two points are separated by 0.5 μ, we can begin to detect them as separate entities.

Interestingly enough, the four principal factors which determine the resolution of the light microscope also determine the resolution of the electron microscope. These factors are (1) diffraction effects, (2) chromatic aberration, (3) spherical aberration, and (4) astigmatism. We shall further see that, in the case of the light microscope, the ultimate resolution is limited by diffraction effects, whereas in present-day electron microscopes the ultimate resolution is limited by spherical aberration of the magnetic lenses.

Diagram A–1 is a schematic representation of the light and electron microscopes. The similarity between the two microscopes is very evident. In both microscopes the source of radiation is a hot tungsten filament. In the light microscope, the light from the hot filament is used to create a final image of the ob-

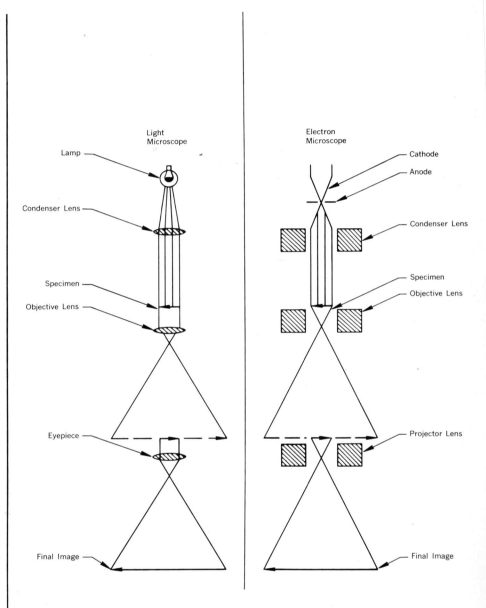

DIAGRAM A–1. Comparison between the components of the light and electron microscopes.

56

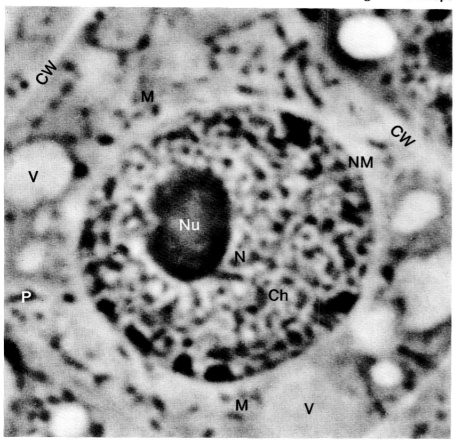

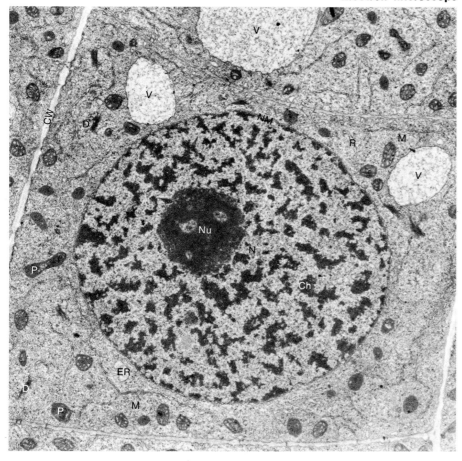

57

FIG. A–1. Comparison of the image obtained from the light and electron microscopes. Both pictures are at the same magnification and have been fixed and prepared in the same way (gluteraldehyde-osmium fixation, epon embedded). The light microscope section was cut at 1.5 micron and photographed in phase contrast. The electron microscope section was cut at 0.03 micron. Both sections were cut from the same piece of tissue. The tissue is an onion root. Visible are the nucleus (N), nucleolus (Nu), chromatin (Ch), nuclear membrane (NM), plastids (P), mitochondria (M), dictyosomes (D), endoplasmic reticulum (ER), vacuoles (V), ribosomes (R), and cell wall (CW). This magnification is the upper limit for the light microscope but is very low magnification for the electron microscope. ×1,000. Photographs, Dr. W. A. Jensen.

ject. In the electron microscope, electrons drawn from the hot filament are used to create the final image. Both microscopes contain a condenser lens to focus incident radiation upon the object being observed. In the light microscope this lens is made of glass. Glass, however, is opaque to electrons, and in the electron microscope the condenser lens is a vertical magnetic field which is provided by passing a current along a coil of wire which is at right angles to the vertical axis of the microscope. After the radiation has passed through the object, the radiation is focused by an objective lens. The final lens of the light microscope is the eyepiece whereas the final lens of the electron microscope is the projector lens. The image of the light microscope may be seen with the eye or projected onto a ground glass screen. The image of the electron microscope, on the other hand, is viewed by allowing the electrons to fall upon a zinc sulfide screen in which molecules excited by the impinging electrons decay to the ground state and thus emit a light visible to the human eye.

In both the light and electron microscopes there would be no image if the object did not in some way interfere with the radiation. In the light microscope, contrast results in part from the absorption of light by molecules in the object, and this light never reaches the final screen. As light quanta pass the edges of objects, diffraction patterns are obtained which are reconstituted by the lens system into an image. Interference effects between the light quanta in this reconstituted image also results in the increased contrast. In the electron microscope, on the other hand, contrast is generally provided by heavy metals which scatter electrons as they pass through the object. These scattered electrons are not refocused on the zinc sulfide screen and, as a result, there are certain areas of the screen which do not light up when the object is being viewed. These dark regions represent areas of the object which contain the heavy metals.

Since the focal length of a glass lens is fixed, the focusing of the light microscope is accomplished by moving the lens an appropriate distance from the object. In the electron microscope, the focal length of the lens may be adjusted according to the amount of current passed through the lens. As a result, the lenses of the electron microscope are not moved in relation to the object; rather, the lens current is changed so as to bring the object into focus.

After this brief description it is possible to consider the reasons for the different resolving power of these two microscopes. The resolution of a microscope, as limited by diffraction effects, is given by the Abbe diffraction equation:

$$d = \frac{0.5\,\lambda}{n\,\text{Sin}\,\alpha}.$$

In this equation d equals the minimum resolvable distance between two objects, λ equals the wave length of radiation used in the microscope, n equals the refractive index of the medium between the object and objective lens, and alpha equals the half aperture angle of the incident radiation. The term $n\,\text{Sin}\,\alpha$ is usually referred to as the numerical aperture (N. A.) of a lens. The highest resolution light microscope lenses' numerical aperture equals about 1.3. Since α in practice can be no greater than about 85° and the maximum refractive index of immersion oil is about 1.5 we can see that the numerical aperture is approximately 0.9 × 1.5 or 1.4 for the light microscope. On the other hand, the minimum wave length of radiation used in the light microscope when the eye is used as a detector is about 4000 A (0.4 μ). Thus, the resolution of the light microscope, as determined by diffraction effects, is

$$d = \frac{0.5 \times 4000\,\text{A}}{1.5 \times \text{Sin}\,85°}.$$

In this case d equals about 2000 A units or 0.2 μ. This same calculation may be made for the electron microscope. Since the electron microscope is evacuated, the refractive index of the medium between the objective lens and the object is 1. The wave length associated with the electron is given by the formula

$$\lambda = \frac{12.3\,\text{A}}{\sqrt{v}},$$

where v is the acceleration voltage of the microscope. Thus, the wave length of the radiation in an electron microscope with an acceleration potential of 50,000 volts equals 0.05 A, whereas the wave length of the radiation in the light microscope was a minimum of 4000 A. It is this difference in wave length which in turn yields the decreased value of d in the Abbe equation. This difference is primarily responsible for the greatly increased resolution of the electron microscope.

Chromatic aberration involves uncertainties in the image due to the fact that lenses have different focal lengths for radiation of different wave lengths. In the light microscope, this means that light of different colors is focused at different distances from the lens. This difficulty has been ingeniously corrected in the light microscope with the use of flint glass lenses in conjunction with the ordinary glass lenses. In the electron microscope, chromatic aberration involves electrons that are accelerated through the microscope at slightly different velocities due to fluctuations in the acceleration voltage. This is corrected in the electron microscope by incorporating a very stable, high voltage power supply. In neither microscope is chromatic aberration a limitation of the ultimate resolution of the instrument.

Astigmatism arises when a lens focuses more strongly along one axis than along the other. As a result, the object can never be clearly focused. This effect can be corrected in both light and electron microscopes.

Spherical aberration occurs when the focal point of the lens depends on the aperture angle of the incident radiation. Thus, light quanta leaving the object and passing close to the center of the lens objective will be focused in one plane while light quanta leaving the object passing through the outer edge of the objective lens will be focused in another plane. This difficulty is not a limitation in a light microscope. However, it is a very severe limitation in the electron microscope since the magnetic field is always much stronger close to the magnet than it is in the center of the magnetic lens. As a result, electrons leaving the object of the electron microscope and passing through the objective magnetic lens experience very different lens strengths when they pass close to the center and when they pass toward the outside of the lens. So far, the only practical way to overcome this difficulty has been to introduce an aperture into the electron microscope which allows only the electrons passing very close to the center of the lens to form a final image. This device, while controlling spherical aberration, severely reduces the resolution of the electron microscope by limiting the numerical aperture. Whereas the resolution of the light microscope was about one-half the wave length of the incident radiation, the resolution of the electron microscope is about 100 times greater than the wave length associated with the electron. The half aperture angle of the electron microscope is on the order of tenths of a degree, while the half aperture angle of the light microscope is 85 degrees. Thus, the limit of resolution of the electron microscope as now constructed is about 5 A. Various devices for increasing the aperture angle of the electron microscope are presently under investigation, and they will eventually allow the resolution of the electron microscope to become considerably greater than it presently is.

Specimen Preparation for the Electron Microscope

We mentioned earlier that specimen contrast in electron microscopy is achieved by incorporating heavy metals into the object under study. At present there are four different techniques utilizing heavy metal incorporation into the specimen which account for almost all the biological electron micrographs now published. These four methods are thin sectioning of fixed tissue, negative staining, heavy metal shadowing, and freeze-etching. All four of these methods are illustrated by the electron micrographs shown in this book.

Thin sectioning. The development of histological techniques in electron microscopy involved three factors. The first was finding appropriate fixatives and stains, the second was achieving a microtome suitable for cutting thin sections required for use in the electron microscope, and the third was the development of suitable embedding media to mount the specimens. The fixatives and stains now commonly used are highly oxidized metallic compounds, such as osmium tetroxide or potassium permanganate. Further contrast may be obtained by post staining with lead or barium compounds. Microtomes utilizing mechanical or thermal advance mechanisms and either broken glass or diamond knives are now available for cutting thin sections from 100–500 A thickness. The embedding medium first used for mounting specimens was methacrylate. In recent years several epoxy resins have been found much more satisfactory for preserving specimen fine structure. In most of the histological examples in this book, material was embedded in epoxy resins. A typical sequence of operations for the embedding and sectioning of biological material for histological electron microscope observation is given in Diagram A–2.

Negative staining techniques. Negative staining differs from the histological techniques in that the electron dense material, rather than being incorporated into specific sites of the biological structure, provides an electron dense background which can be displaced by the biological structure. A negative stained preparation can be seen in Fig. 11–3. In this case, a thin layer of phosphotungstic acid surrounds the components of a bacterial cell wall. The entire background appears electron dense, while the areas occupied by the biological molecules appear electron transparent. As a result, the image,

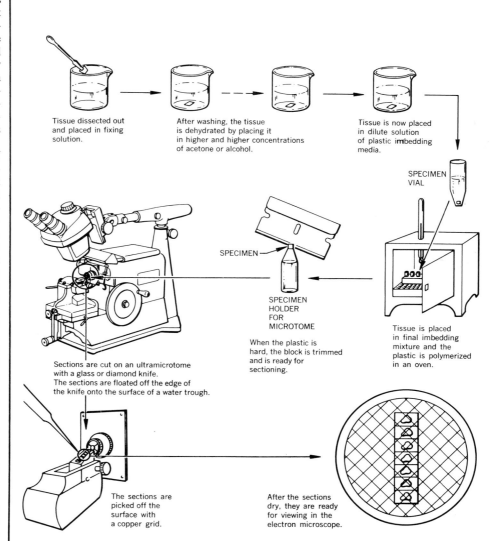

Tissue dissected out and placed in fixing solution.

After washing, the tissue is dehydrated by placing it in higher and higher concentrations of acetone or alcohol.

Tissue is now placed in dilute solution of plastic imbedding media.

SPECIMEN VIAL

SPECIMEN

SPECIMEN HOLDER FOR MICROTOME

When the plastic is hard, the block is trimmed and is ready for sectioning.

Tissue is placed in final imbedding mixture and the plastic is polymerized in an oven.

Sections are cut on an ultramicrotome with a glass or diamond knife. The sections are floated off the edge of the knife onto the surface of a water trough.

The sections are picked off the surface with a copper grid.

After the sections dry, they are ready for viewing in the electron microscope.

DIAGRAM A–2. Embedding and sectioning of biological material for histological electron microscope observation.

59

when viewed in the electron microscope, appears dark except for those areas occupied by the specimen where the heavy metal has been excluded. The heavy metals used in negative staining are often phosphotungstate or various uranium salts.

Heavy metal shadowing. Heavy metal shadowing is one of the oldest methods of preparing biological material for electron microscopy. This method involves laying the material on a thin plastic or carbon supporting film and then casting a thin metal film over the specimen in a vacuum. This operation is illustrated in Diagram A–3. Image contrast is provided by the metal which builds up on the front side of the specimen and is absent on the side away from the hot filament.

Freeze-etching. Freeze-etching is a relatively new technique which provides contrast by utilizing the method of heavy metal shadowing. The specimen, however, is uniquely prepared. Specimens are rapidly frozen and then sectioned in an evacuated chamber with a microtome at minus 100°. The microtome rather than making a smooth cut actually fractures the surface of the specimen along planes of natural weakness. The planes of natural weakness tend to run along membrane faces—for example, along the endoplasmic reticulum, or over or under the nucleus, or over or under a mitochondrion. The membranes usually split down the center. A great deal of detail is evident on the faces of these membranes. This view is almost impossible to achieve by histological techniques, for they show membranes best in cross section. Once the fracturing is completed, a small amount of water is sublimed from the exposed face and a combination of platinum and carbon is shadow cast upon the surface. The specimen is then removed from the vacuum chamber and the biological material is digested away from the underside of the surface replica. The cleaned replica is recovered and placed in the electron microscope for observation. Thus far, this method represents our closest approximation to observing high resolution details inside living cells. In the case of yeast and many bacteria, the cells sectioned in the microtome are potentially living. If such cells are removed and warmed to room temperature, a large percentage continue to grow. Thus the freeze-etch replica, unlike other preparative procedures, yields a section through a potentially living system.   ●

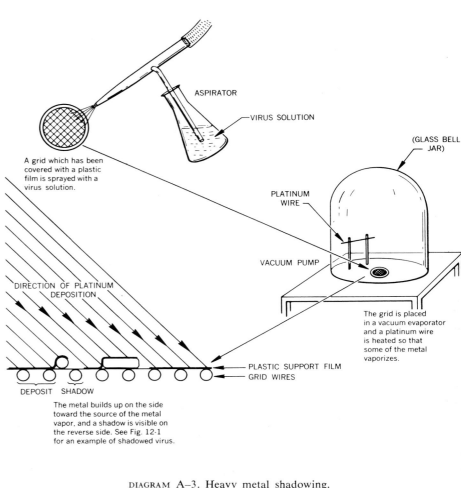

DIAGRAM A–3. Heavy metal shadowing.

SUGGESTED READINGS

GENERAL

KAY, D. H. *Techniques for Electron Microscopy.* Philadelphia: F. A. Davis Co., 1965. A collection of papers on a wide range of techniques used in electron microscopy, including cytochemical methods.

PEASE, D. C. *Histological Techniques for Electron Microscopy.* New York: Academic Press, Inc., 1964. The "bible" of electron microscopists, written by a pioneer in the field.

WISCHNITZER, S. *Introduction to Electron Microscopy.* New York: Pergamon Press, Inc., 1962. An excellent short book on the theory and practice of the operation of the electron microscope, written for the biologist.

TECHNICAL

MOOR, H., AND K. MÜHLETHALER. "Fine Structure in Frozen-etched Yeast Cells." *Jour. Cell Biol.* Vol. 17 (1963), pp. 609–628. A discussion of the basis of the freeze-etch procedure and the results obtained by its use.